Rowena Summers
Taking Heart

CANELO

First published in Great Britain in 2000 by Severn House Publishers

This edition published in the United Kingdom in 2023 by

Canelo
Unit 9, 5th Floor
Cargo Works, 1–2 Hatfields
London SE1 9PG
United Kingdom

A CIP catalogue record for this book is available from the British Library.

Print ISBN 978 1 80436 543 4
Ebook ISBN 978 1 80436 290 7

Look for more great books at www.canelo.co

Printed and bound in Great Britain by Clays Ltd, Elcograf S.p.A.

1

But only temporarily. Only until whole livelihoods were turned upside-down, and someone had the unpleasant task of relaying the news to his family as gently as possible. And to Quentin the family had always meant everything.

"Why so gloomy, Father?" his eldest and best-beloved daughter Imogen asked him with a smile. "It's such a lovely day; tell us what's so important so that we can all go out and enjoy it."

"I wanted Baz to be here first," Quentin said with a frown. "The boy has no sense of time."

"You won't tear him away from his old boats on a day like this," eighteen-year-old Elsie chipped in. "He'll happily spend all his spare time chatting with the ferrymen on the river, and nothing's going to change that."

Imogen hoped Elsie's words wouldn't upset their father. His shop was his pride, and despite having three vivacious daughters he hoped and expected that his son Baz would eventually take it over and carry on the family tradition. But Imogen was all too well aware that at nearly fifteen, and with schooldays behind him, Baz had definite ideas of his own. The lure of the fast-flowing river Avon and the old salts, who passed on tales of adventure that went back into history, had captured his imagination far more than the idea of working in a clothing and haber-dashery shop. They all knew it, even if their father refused to acknowledge it.

"Anyway," Daisy said, precocious at sixteen, and tossing back the russet curls that were her current vanity, "whatever the news is, it can't be anything *too* terrible!"

Her father said nothing.

Imogen felt a sharp stab of fear and knew the truth of the old saying of a goose walking over her grave. She was more perceptive than her sisters and, seeing her mother

Chapter One

As the family gathered in the sitting-room of the tall Bristol house that Sunday afternoon, Quentin Caldwell looked at his three daughters with immense satisfaction and pride. There were none who could touch them for beauty as well as brains – and that was rare enough. Women were not supposed to have any intelligence at all, or if they did, they were not supposed to show it. He prided himself that they got the brains from himself, while the looks were all down to his beautiful wife.

At the thought, his composure slipped a little. Frances was so frail and delicate now, her smile alarmingly vacant as she quietly hummed a ditty from the far-off days when she had danced on the stage in front of royalty. Quentin knew she was still there in her dreams.

Such royalty, too, he mused. So many changes, in so short a time. The sad death of the old king had plunged the country into mourning, followed by excitement over whether the dashing Prince of Wales would be crowned Edward the Seventh, or give way to his passion for Mrs Simpson. And then there had been the uproar and scandal when he abdicated and the new and hesitant George the Sixth had been crowned.

Such momentous matters of state – and the wild speculation surrounding them – could put the modest affairs of people like themselves into a different perspective drifting off into a world of her own as she gazed unseeingly out of the window as if to shut out everything else, she knew that something was terribly wrong.

It wasn't her mother, was it…? But something was going to affect them all, and Imogen felt the strongest instinct to put her arms around all of them and protect them from whatever it was.

As the door burst open, she turned with a feeling of relief as her strapping young brother breezed into the room. He was closely followed by five-year-old Teddy, inevitably still trailing his blanket behind him.

Teddy's traumatic birth had caused the mental and physical affliction that had gradually turned their mother into the frail creature she was now. To his credit, their father had never blamed the boy, but nor did he give him the attention he deserved, with the result that Imogen and her sisters had initially lavished far more affection on Teddy than was good for him, and Quentin told them more than once that they were in danger of turning the child into a monster.

"So you've decided to join us, have you?" Quentin said to Baz now.

The fact that he spoke so mildly and didn't censure him added to Imogen's sense of impending disaster. She couldn't shake it off. Moments before, it seemed, the midsummer day had been so blue and sunny. It still was, and yet to her it was as if a big dark cloud had obscured the sun, though she couldn't say why.

"Take the child to the nursery, Imogen," her father went on, before Baz could make any sparky reply. "No, wait," he added, as Frances's incessant humming grew louder. "Your mother had better go too. It's time for her nap, anyway. Ring for Miss Lindsey to see to them both."

Imogen pressed the bell at once, thinking it heartbreaking that her once so-beautiful mother should be reduced to the status of a child with needs as simple as Teddy's. But she knew it was true. When the doctor had stated plainly and bluntly that Frances's mental state was declining rapidly into some kind of dreamland, the nurse-companion had become very necessary for both of them.

More than any of the others, Imogen remembered her mother as she had once been, enchanting them with her dancing at Christmas time and on birthdays, and entertaining them at the piano in the sweet voice that Daisy had inherited. Frances was softly singing a half-remembered song from those lost days now, but the mumbling words were no more than a parody of the lyrics she had once known so well.

Quentin swiftly crossed to his wife and drew her away from the window.

"It's time to stop that now, Frances," he said, his voice more husky than before.

"Stop what, my dear?"

He squeezed her hand before raising it to his lips. It was an old-fashioned, loving gesture that tugged at Imogen's heart, and from the way her sisters averted their eyes, she knew they felt it too.

"Your singing is purer than a nightingale's, my love," Quentin went on gently. "But perhaps you could treat us to it another time."

She nodded happily, and crossed her small delicate hands together, as demure as a nun. She was so thin now, her limbs so brittle that they almost seemed in danger of breaking if anyone hugged her too tightly. It was a relief when the nurse-companion came to take her and the complaining Teddy away.

"Well, thank goodness he's gone," Baz said feelingly. "He clings to me like glue lately."

"That's because you're his hero," Daisy said with a giggle. "You should be flattered, brother dear!"

"Well, I'm not," Baz retorted. "I don't care to be seen with an infant tagging along at my heels all the time. My friends will think I'm a milksop."

"Seeing that most of your friends are those burly riverside fellows, and that you can keep up with them with your banter *and* your fists from all I hear, I doubt that there's any danger of that," his father said crisply. "But now that we're all here, it's time to get down to business. I wanted you all here together for a very special reason."

He looked round at them again, knowing he was about to shatter their world, and thinking that he would give anything he owned to spare them what was to come.

His lovely girls were like three beautiful butterflies in their summer frocks, their complexions as fresh and clear as their mother's ever had been, the three pairs of doe-soft brown eyes looking at him with expectancy and curiosity. Especially Imogen, his Immy. He knew she must have a shrewd idea that they weren't meeting just to spend a Sunday afternoon together.

They were all growing up so fast. Even Baz was almost a man – and showed such assurance, he had to admit. The boy was lounging against the window now, his attention still drawn to far below the crowded hillside street where they lived, across the great seafaring city of Bristol, to the river whose whiff could be sensed even up here. And no matter how tainted or rank it was, it still seemed as pure as the finest wine to his son.

"Please come and sit down, Baz," he said abruptly. "I need everyone's full attention."

Baz flopped into an armchair, his thoughts diverted from how soon he could broach the subject of working for one of the ferrymen instead of continuing behind the shop counter, which in his opinion was no occupation for a young man. Let the girls do it, he thought loftily. They seemed to enjoy it well enough, especially when any of the young men of the town brought their mamas in to browse for their fripperies.

Daisy wasn't averse to flirting with them, flashing her big eyes at them and pushing out her small bosom as far as it would go. Baz sniggered to himself, feeling a tug in his loins at the thought. Not with regard to his *sister*, of course, but remembering some of the tales the sailors told him about the women in every port, and the games they got up to.

Elsie wasn't interested in flirting, as far as he knew, though you never knew much about what Elsie was thinking. And Immy was already secretly courting a young man. He knew, even if no one else did.

He'd followed them one day and seen how Morgan Raine had pushed his laughing sister down into the hollow on the grassy hill above their street and covered her mouth with kisses. She hadn't objected either, and he doubted that their father would be pleased to know of it. It was a little piece of information Baz was keeping up his sleeve in case he should ever need it.

"Are you actually *with* us, Baz?" he heard his father say more sharply, and he pulled his thoughts back to the sitting-room where everyone was looking at him now. He felt his face redden, thankful that they couldn't see into his mind.

"I'm sorry, Father. I'm all yours," he said quickly.

Daisy giggled, and he glared at her. But some of Immy's anxiety was starting to transmit to all of them now, and she glared back at him.

Their father cleared his throat, picked up a pile of papers from a side table and shuffled them.

"I've had several lengthy discussions with our accountant, my dears. I won't bother you with all the details, but since Immy has been dealing with the business side of the shop lately, she can go through the figures later and see that what I'm about to tell you cannot be changed."

"Why should Immy understand things any better than the rest of us?" Baz said at once.

"Because you've never shown the slightest interest in figures, and it's a little late to start now."

Baz's face reddened still more, even though he knew the slight was true. He was a dunce when it came to figures; his skills were more practical.

"Listen to what Father has to say, Baz." His oldest sister turned on him. "What do you do to earn your keep, anyway? You're always down at the river—"

"I don't have to do anything to earn my keep yet!" Baz whipped back. "That's what fathers are for!"

As Elsie gasped and Daisy's hands flew to her mouth, their normally tolerant father lunged at him.

"You insufferable young prig! You'll be eating those words before this meeting's finished."

"If it ever gets started," Baz muttered, crimson now, and knowing he'd gone too far.

"Then let me start it at once by telling you that you will very soon have to think about earning your keep, my boy, because we are in serious financial trouble."

"What!" Imogen gasped. "But we can't be."

"Daddy, that can't be true," Elsie said uneasily. "The shop has always done good business – and still does, surely."

"Caldwell's Supplies – or 'the shop', as you all persist in calling it – will not continue to do the business that will keep us all in the same standard of living we've always enjoyed for much longer."

"What does that mean, exactly?" Daisy said, nervous now as the nightmare prospect of having to be a penny-pincher like the people who lived in hovels along the riverside suddenly dawned on her.

"Well, I don't see how there can be any problem," Baz put in, determined to show that he was sufficiently involved in the business to know what was what. "There's never a shortage of customers and we've always been on good terms with our regulars, so I don't see—"

"That's the trouble. You never see what's not right beneath your nose," Quentin retorted. "If it doesn't smell of fish, or have two oars and a few fathoms of water beneath it, you don't want to know, do you?"

"Well, I know it suits the girls, but I never wanted to stand behind a shop counter for the rest of my life," Baz retorted, too wound up now to mind what he was saying. "Any ignorant female could do that!"

"Well, thank you!" Daisy said indignantly. "You've got a nerve, Baz Caldwell. I'd say any idiot could row a boat and ferry a few paying passengers from one side of the river to the other. Where's the skill in *that*?"

"Will you please calm down?" Quentin begged as their voices rose. "We're not going to get anywhere if we all shout at one another. I want no squabbling, and I need to tell you what's to be done."

"Is it all cut and dried then, Father?" Imogen asked.

"There was no choice," he answered, his voice as flat as if someone had stamped on it.

In the small silence that followed, Elsie, normally the quietest of them all, spoke more assertively than usual.

"Won't you please tell us what's happened, Daddy? Nobody's fatally ill, or going to die, are they?"

They all looked at him as her words fell away, their thoughts immediately flying to their mother. As if he knew at once where their anxieties would lie, he shook his head.

"Nobody's ill or going to die, my loves," he said more gently. "But we're going to have to make a change in our circumstances."

"But *why*?" Elsie persisted, for once taking charge of the questioning, since the others seemed to have been temporarily silenced. "What's happened?"

"What's happened – is Preston's Emporium."

As they stared at him, he gave a resigned sigh. And to Imogen's eyes, he seemed to shrink physically from the larger-than-life figure they all knew.

"You'll all have heard of the name," he said at last.

"Of course," said Immy. "It's been mentioned enough in the retail circular. Its owners seem to have bought up half the North, if you believe their boastfulness."

"Believe it, darling," Quentin said heavily.

"You're not saying they want to buy out our lease, are you, Father?" Imogen asked quickly, when no one else seemed willing to put the thought into words.

"They buy out whatever and wherever they want to, apparently. And now they're coming south to build on their little empire."

"But they're a northern company," Baz burst out, wanting to prove that he knew at least something about the retail trade. "They've never opened shops in the South before, have they? It must be a mistake."

"It's no mistake. We're only leaseholders of the property, and Preston's are intending to buy out the entire row of shops and turn it into another Emporium, which will establish them in Bristol."

"Well, why can't we just open another shop somewhere else?" Daisy said at once.

Quentin chewed his lip. "I'm afraid that's not possible, my love. It pains me to have to tell my children of our financial situation, but in recent years we've had to take far more out of the business than has been coming in. And then there were the riots last year, when we had to replace all the broken windows and the shop front and restock after the looting."

Immy guessed where the other expenses were coming from. Their mother's medical bills were heavy, and so was the salary for the nurse-companion who looked after her and Teddy. She ached that her father was obliged to explain all this to them.

"What does the landlord have to say about it?"

"A verbal apology, followed by a letter of explanation," her father said, suddenly bitter. "But since he'll make a killing from Preston's, I suppose you can't blame him."

"Well, I think it stinks," Baz said passionately.

"Do you, Baz?" his father queried with the glimmer of a smile. "That's the most encouraging thing I've heard you say yet about Caldwell's Supplies."

"It won't be that any longer, will it?" Elsie said sadly. "*We* won't be Caldwell's Supplies any longer, will we? It will be Preston's. Will we have to work for them now?"

"Well, *I* won't," Baz raged.

"None of us will," Quentin said carefully. "But I'm afraid you haven't heard the worst of it yet. We have been living on credit for some time, and there are simply too many debts for us to continue living in this house."

"*What!*"

He couldn't have said which of his children spoke first, since the sound seemed to be a collective cry that tore at his heart. He was a proud man who had always provided for his family, and never had he felt such a failure as he did at that moment.

Immy's throat was tight, but she knew she spoke for all of them. "Father, you can't mean it. It will break Mother's heart if we have to leave here."

"There are other houses, my dear. Other parts of the world that are just as beautiful as Bristol. Look how your Aunt Rose and Uncle Bertie have settled in Weston-super-Mare. You've all enjoyed visiting them at the seaside."

"You're not suggesting we go and live in Weston-super-Mare, are you?" Baz said at once. "I won't go, anyway."

"I'm not suggesting it," Quentin reassured him. "I'm merely pointing out that a house is just a house. It's the people inside it who make it a home."

"But there's no place where Mother will feel as comfortable as she does under Doctor Wolfe's care," Elsie pointed out, her voice catching.

Daisy went to her father and put her arms around him, pleading with him. "Daddy, please don't say we have to leave here. I couldn't bear it."

"You'll find young men to flirt with wherever you go, ninny," Baz said, lashing out in his bewilderment.

Daisy ignored him, but Immy too felt her heart sink. Leaving Bristol would mean leaving Morgan Raine, and she was still only on the brink of love and learning what it meant to feel like a grown-up woman from the more experienced Morgan.

She wouldn't have known what to expect if she hadn't discovered the slim booklet inside a brown envelope in Baz's bedroom one day recently, detailing the kind of intimate information best kept out of childish heads. He had sworn it had been loaned to him by a boy from his old school, and she had demanded he give it back at once.

Before she'd confronted Baz, however, she had taken a sneaking look through the pages herself and been astonished and embarrassed at what she had learned, since sex education didn't enter the Caldwell household.

Her father would probably deny that physical intimacy had ever taken place between himself and his wife, Imogen thought, trying to diffuse her heightened senses with some cynical amusement. As if all the children had been virgin births. She immediately felt her heartbeat quicken uneasily at the unconscious blasphemy of such a thought. But it was true that the frank details of how love could be expressed between a man and a woman was simply something she could never have asked her mother about, even when Frances had been sensible enough to answer them.

So Imogen had been left as ignorant as Baz and the rest of them, until Morgan Raine had begun to enlighten her about what their vicar would undoubtedly call the sins of the flesh – which didn't seem at all sinful to Imogen and were deliciously intoxicating to the senses.

As the memories threatened to make her head go dizzy, she forced her mind back to the present, and what was happening here in this room today.

What Elsie had said was true. Her mother relied heavily on the family doctor for her welfare. She trusted him, and a less caring physician would have suggested long ago that Frances Caldwell's mind was wandering so rapidly that she would be better off with specialist care in an institution.

None of them dared say it, of course. But they must all realise now that whatever debts had been incurred during recent months, much of it must be due to the medical bills, and to Miss Lindsey's exorbitant salary, as the nurse-companion their father insisted that their mother needed.

"Father, if the worst comes to the worst—" Imogen began, hardly knowing what she intended to say, but knowing she had to say something to take away the grey-ness of his face.

"It's already here, my love."

But Imogen was nothing if not practical and quick-thinking. If a thing could not be saved, then you had to think of something else to take its place. A compromise that was half as good, or even better.

The shock of losing the business seemed inevitable and was a trauma they would all have to deal with, but it was receding a little in her mind now and being taken over by her reaction to her father's decision about the house.

"I agree with Elsie and Daisy that Mother will hate having to leave here, and it's surely the last thing we want. There's a way out of that, if you would only consider it."

"If you're a miracle worker, my dear, then let's hear it," he said without any conviction.

"Why couldn't we take in paying guests? It's a perfectly respectable situation, and the house is large enough."

The reaction was instant. "*Lodgers*, you mean? Have strangers living in the house, and have to share the bathroom and your mother's kitchen with them, and finding them underfoot every time we turned around? Your mother would hate it, and I certainly won't have strangers treating her like an – an – imbecile, because of her odd ways!"

He suddenly choked, and she was the one now to put her arms around him and hug him.

"Daddy, please don't dismiss it out of hand," she said quietly. "This part of Bristol is familiar to Mother, and it's about the only thing that is now. Sometimes she seems hardly aware of us these days, and she behaves towards us as if *we're* the strangers."

She knew he didn't like what he was hearing, but she plunged on. "As for her kitchen – well, I know you like to think that on Cook's afternoon off Mother does a little baking herself, but Miss Lindsey can't be her eyes and ears all the time, and one of these days I think Mother will either gas herself or set the house on fire!"

She spoke recklessly, but she should have known his response to any censure of his adored wife. He shook her off, his eyes flashing angrily – but before he could say anything Baz had put in his spoke.

"It's not such a bad idea, Father. You'd need to know the people had good pedigrees, of course, but I daresay Immy would see to that, since she's so good at organising."

"Of course I would," Imogen replied, not rising to his bait. She was just thankful to have an ally, however unlikely – and however much Baz was acting in his own interest, of course, she added silently. Baz wouldn't want to move too far away from his beloved river.

"We'd have to interview them to see that they had impeccable references," she went on, improvising quickly. "They would be elderly ladies or gentlemen with means, or respectable couples, or even theatrical people from the Old Vic. I'm sure that would please Mother. It would make her feel that she still had a toe in the door of her old life."

She held her breath as her words sank into her father's brain – and her own. The idea had quickly taken hold of her, and she couldn't see anything wrong with it. Sometimes the best ideas were the ones that came spontaneously. Her mother used to say it was as if fate was giving you a little prod in the right direction, and like Frances, Imogen was a great believer in fate.

As for the shop…well, they all knew that the shop was the fulfilment of their father's ambition, not theirs. Baz wanted to be out of it altogether, and she suspected Daisy had always had secret hankerings to follow a stage career. There were always auditions being held at the Hippodrome and the Old Vic, and who knew where her pretty sister might go if she got the chance?

Elsie was clever at hat-making and took orders from many of the well-to-do ladies who frequented the shop. She could surely pursue that idea. Then there was herself… What was for her? What did she really want out of life?

She felt a sudden small thrill of excitement in her veins. Her young man, Morgan, worked in the print shop of a local newspaper: and perhaps she too could find some kind of work to do with journalism. It must be exciting to interview people, to attend dramatic events and report back to the newspaper, and to see your name in print.

More realistically, she knew that was most unlikely to happen. Young ladies didn't usually become proper journalists – but she had learned shorthand in order to take down customers' orders speedily, and she could type on her father's old black typewriter, so perhaps she could start off in a lowly department and work her way up. Maybe.

"This needs a good deal of thinking about."

She heard her father speak as if from a great distance, and she realised she had been totally wrapped up in her own thoughts for the last few minutes, dreaming of an ambition she'd never known she possessed. Until now. Until the chance had come to break out from a family business and follow dreams of her own.

Guilt immediately flooded through her mind. How could she be so ungrateful, when their father had provided a loving home and a comfortable living for all of them – until now? But until now, none of them had even thought of breaking away. Except Baz, of course – and she had no real idea of what her sisters might be thinking, come to that.

She wouldn't know, until they left the room and had a chance to talk about it among themselves.

"Perhaps we all need to go away and think about things," she said helpfully.

To her surprise, her father was nodding thoughtfully, looking a mite less harassed than before. Bringing bad news out into the open always helped. It was a trouble shared, and all that rot, Immy thought. Even if you didn't always want to have to share it…

"If I'm to take this scheme of yours seriously, Immy," he said slowly, "there are a few other things to consider. In normal circumstances I wouldn't dream of dispensing with your mother's companion. But there'll be no need to keep her on when the shop goes, because none of you will be working there. Your younger sisters can help with the household chores, and you can take over Miss Lindsey's duties—"

Imogen gave a loud cry as all her fleeting, half-formed dreams of independence melted away in an instant.

"You could also teach Teddy his letters and numbers until he goes to school," her father went on blandly.

"Father, you can't mean that," she gasped. "I'll be little more than a housemaid!"

"And so will we," Daisy cried. "How will we ever meet young men, if we're stuck indoors all day with old people and boring lodgers?"

"Is that all you think of caring for your mother?"

"I didn't mean Mother," Daisy said, scarlet-faced. "I meant the strangers Immy wants to fill the house with!"

"You were all for it just now," Imogen snapped.

"Well, I'm not anymore," Daisy sulked.

"And neither am I," said Elsie.

Baz snorted. "Well, I can't see anything wrong with it."

"You wouldn't!" Daisy rounded on him, all spiky curls and bristling temper. "You won't be here all day. You'll be out on your precious ferry-boats with those dreadful men you call your friends, all smelling of fish and the river—"

They suddenly realised that their father was laughing softly as the four of them wrangled.

"Daisy, my love, you do my heart good. You're such a terrible snob, and no one will ever get the better of you!"

"All the same, Father," Immy said quickly, deciding to leave the uncertain question of her own future for the moment, "I think you're wrong to think about getting rid of Miss Lindsey. Mother does need professional help.

Sometimes she wanders out of the house alone when Miss Lindsey's taking her nap, and we've had to search for her to bring her back."

His mood changed like quicksilver.

"*What?* Why haven't I been told this before? That incompetent woman must be dismissed, and without references."

"She's not incompetent. She's just exhausted from the worry of trying to keep Mother safe," Immy told him.

"Well, she obviously hasn't succeeded if she lets her go wandering about the city," he snapped.

He swallowed convulsively. The house wasn't too far from the river, and the thought of where Frances might end up was suddenly all too graphic in his mind.

But he was determined not to give way to an emotional breakdown in front of his children. He waved them away and told them to leave him to think.

"And you might all do a deal of thinking as well," he added. "We all have to make sacrifices in this world, and it's never too early for you to discover it. Life has been easy for you until now, but only a fool or an optimist believes it will always be so."

Chapter Two

The four of them walked down to the river, where they usually did their thinking. Fishing boats and larger vessels jostled for position in the harbour, and sailors of every nationality jawed among themselves on the waterfront.

The aroma of fetid ale rose from the gutters, and the riverside women eyed the foursome with varying degrees of interest. It wasn't the most salubrious place to take a walk, and in the heat of the July sun, the stink was high – but none of the Caldwell family noticed it.

"It's not fair," Daisy burst out at last. "Daddy should never have let things get as bad as they have."

"None of it was his fault," Immy said, defending him at once. "You talk about being fair, but he couldn't have stopped Preston's Emporium bidding for the row of shops. He couldn't prevent the riots, either. Think about his feelings for a minute, Daisy, and not so much about your own."

"But he shouldn't have got into so much debt. Mother—"

"Are you saying he shouldn't have hired Miss Lindsey to care for Mother?" Elsie returned at once.

Imogen interrupted. "I'm sure we all agree that Mother should have *someone* caring for her, but Miss Lindsey must be a terrible drain on Father. She instructs Cook to buy all sorts of exotic food for Mother's delicate stomach, and then there's the ridiculous dress allowance she requested because of the way Mother upsets things over her precious clothes. She behaves more like the lady of the house than Mother herself."

"Well, at least you need have no fears that Daddy's thinking of installing her as a paramour should anything happen to Mother," Elsie said primly. "He's made it patently obvious that he can't stand her airs and graces, and only tolerates her because Mother relies on her so much."

"But that's just it, isn't it? Mother adores her, and Miss Lindsey knows it," Immy muttered. "How is she going to react when Father gets rid of her?"

"What's a paramour?" Baz asked. He had been too enmeshed in his own thoughts to pay much heed to what the others were saying, but his attention was caught by the erotic sound of the word.

"None of your business," Imogen said smartly, with a warning look at the others as they started laughing. "Anyway, why don't you go and find something to do, Baz? I'm sure all this serious talk is boring you," she added sarcastically.

"No, it's not."

"*Go!*" she said. "And I may just agree to have a game of draughts with you after tea."

Seeing that he always won, it was enough of a bribe, and after a few minutes she saw him talking animatedly with the old fishermen on the quay. Baz would find his feet, no matter what happened, she thought fleetingly.

She turned to her sisters as they sat down on one of the benches on the waterfront.

"Daddy wouldn't have to sell the car, would he?" Daisy said suddenly, aghast at the thought. "It would be such a let-down. I don't think I could bear to be poor—"

"You really are impossible sometimes, Daisy," Immy told her sharply. "There are plenty of people poorer than us, and in any case we all have feet – and bicycles. But selling the car would be the last thing Father would do, I'm sure. Mother does so enjoy being taken out for rides."

As Daisy fell silent at the rebuke, Immy went on determinedly, "So what do you think about the idea of taking in paying guests? I only said it on the spur of the moment, but the more I think about it, the more it makes sense."

"I'm not sure, Immy," Elsie said dubiously. "If Daddy's idea is to move into a smaller house, I assume he wants to dismiss the housekeeper and cut Cook's hours. If we take in paying guests, we'll probably end up employing more people than we do now."

"Unless Immy takes over all the household duties," Daisy said slyly. "As well as looking after Mother and Teddy too, of course. She could get paid a proper salary then. What do you say to that, Immy?"

Immy gave another smart reply. "Definitely not! I'll help Father all I can, but I've no intention of doing everything. You two will have to do your share."

She felt a pang of regret at the thought. It was all a far cry from her little dream of joining the newspaper trade. The charm of working beside Morgan hadn't escaped her; there would be a legitimate reason for seeing him every single day, instead of at snatched, secret moments.

When they weren't kissing and cuddling, he sometimes told her about the excitement of working in the news-paper office. It wasn't all local stuff, he'd say loftily. They got wind of troubles in Europe long before the ordinary public, and, in his opinion, they were heading for war.

It was then that Immy shivered. She preferred the love-talk and the kissing and cuddling to when Morgan got all pompous and serious. She *much* preferred it to any talk of war…although there were murmurings of it everywhere, and strong disapproval of the way Mr Hitler was becoming such a dictator. But Europe and its problems seemed very far away when you had never in your life travelled further than twenty miles or so to the coast of the Bristol Channel.

"Well, I didn't want to work in a shop all my life anyway. I shall look for a proper job now," Daisy declared, lifting her chin defiantly.

"Oh, yes? Doing what, darling?" Elsie asked her in amusement. "All you *know* is serving behind a shop counter."

"I might see if there's any work at one of the theatres. They must need somebody to make tea or paint scenery or be a prompt. I might even offer to be an unpaid under-study – just for a short time – until I'm discovered, and they realise they've got a second Sarah Bernhardt right under their noses!" she added, as theatrically as could be.

The other two laughed at her nonsense. But if anybody had the guts to pull her socks up and do exactly what she intended, Daisy did, thought Immy.

"Of course, failing that, I might just go and ask Preston's to give me a job," she went on casually, testing the water for a reaction.

"Oh no you don't!" Immy snapped. "It would be like slapping Father in the face. You hear me, Daisy?"

Elsie agreed. "Immy's right. We all have to stick together. If Daddy decides to go ahead with the paying-guest idea, and if we have to do some of the work for some of the time, that's what we'll have to do."

"Hooray!" Immy put in, pleasantly surprised that Elsie should feel strongly enough to take a stand.

Suddenly they became aware that they were the objects of attention from a small group of swaggering seamen from one of the container ships that regularly came into the city docks to unload goods and materials. The men stood squarely in front of them, blotting out the sunlight and grinning down at them.

"Now that's what I call a sight for sore eyes, ain't it, lads? Three beauties with hair like fire, and as lush a trio of peaches as I ever did see."

"True enough, Sven. And just ripe for the plucking," one of his companions said with a snigger.

The first accent wasn't English. Like the second it was coarse and guttural, and Imogen seethed at the way the men laughed at their own joke, looking her and her sisters over as if they were prime specimens of cod on fishmonger Lacey's marble slab.

She heard Daisy give a nervous giggle and knew that given half a chance her sister would react to these louts and start up a conversation that would soon degenerate. There was something wild about Daisy that needed to be curbed...

Just listen to yourself! Immy thought in disgust. Thinking like a maiden aunt, when she was only a month off her twentieth birthday.

"And where are you three beauties going on a fine day like this?" the second man leered. "If you're looking for company, petals, we've got a couple of hours to spare."

But Elsie too had had enough of these oafs and was already standing up, brushing down the skirt of her cotton dress and tossing back her hair as defiantly as Daisy ever did.

"It's time we went," she said firmly. "Come on, Daisy. Come *on*!" she added as her sister lingered.

They heard the catcalls of the men behind them but took no notice as they linked arms and strode off along the waterfront. They had no idea where Baz had gone; he considered himself too old now to be seen for too long in the company of his sisters.

"Don't take any notice," Immy instructed as the whistles followed them. "They've got too much time on their hands, and there are other girls for what they want."

"What *do* they want, Immy?" Daisy said, far too innocently.

"You'll find out when you're old enough and not before."

"Don't treat me like a baby! When I'm rich and famous—"

The words brought Immy up short. "Oh, please, spare us the theatricals! There are far more important things to think about – like how we're going to persuade Father not to give up the house, for a start."

And how could we have forgotten, even for a minute!

"You really are set on this paying-guest idea, aren't you, Immy?" Elsie said. "But I must admit I'm a bit squeamish at the thought of sharing a bathroom with strangers."

"There's always the old privy at the bottom of the yard, if you're so fussy."

"It wouldn't worry me," Daisy said airily. "When Mother was on the stage I know she shared rooms with all sorts of other people. It's what theatrical folk do."

She stopped abruptly as the image of her once lovely mother surged into her mind. In the box of mementoes

Frances had hoarded there were posters of her in her spangly costumes, and theatre programmes with her name quite prominent. As a young child Daisy had been enchanted by the images and pictured herself doing exactly what her mother had done – singing and dancing to the crowds and receiving their applause. She had thought then that it was glamorous and exciting, and she still did.

She felt Immy's hand on her arm, squeezing it tight.

"We all feel sad for Mother," Imogen said quietly. "But nothing can change what's happened, and we all have to go on and do the best we can, don't we?"

"I suppose so," said Daisy, blinking back the sudden blurring in her eyes.

"And right now we have to be strong for Father's sake. He must have felt terrible when he first realised how bad things were, and even if this doesn't work, just giving him the idea of doing something positive will revive his spirits."

"You're always so wise, Immy," Elsie said approvingly.

"Oh Elsie, for pity's sake don't make me sound like a saint," Imogen replied, irritated rather than pleased at this reaction. "I'm just thinking practically, that's all. None of us wants to leave the house, and anything's better than having to decamp down to Weston to move in with Aunt Rose and Uncle Bertie, isn't it?"

Daisy giggled. "You'd better not let Daddy hear you say that about his dear sister. I thought you liked them!"

"Of course I like them. But the thought of all of us cramped into that house of theirs doesn't thrill me."

"The beach is nice, though," Elsie said reflectively. "All that lovely sand – and the donkey rides for Teddy—"

"And all that mud when the tide goes out," Daisy added.

"Maybe if the worst comes to the worst and we *are* obliged to move to a smaller place, we should consider living there. Mother's always been very fond of Aunt Rose. Perhaps we could even open a tea-room on the seafront," Elsie went on, determined not to let her sister be the only one with ideas. "What do you say, Immy?"

Daisy squealed before she could answer. "It's a perfectly horrid idea! It's all right in the summer, but in the winter there's nothing to do. I don't want to live in the sticks, so don't you dare suggest it!"

But Immy was no longer listening to either of them. By now they had walked back from the waterfront towards the city, intending to join the folk who paraded about the town on Sunday afternoons. They headed towards the marketplace at Welsh Back, where the boats from Wales traditionally brought their goods for sale. But not today, of course. On Sundays the marketplace was washed clean, empty of fish and produce, and was a meeting place for young men and their lady friends.

And strolling along one of the alleyways leading off it, a young man was leaning towards a pretty young girl with hair the colour of corn, his arm loosely around her waist as she laughed up into his face. Moments later they had turned a corner and were out of sight.

"What's wrong, Immy?" Elsie said, suddenly aware of her sister's quickened breathing and painfully flushed face. "Have you seen someone you know?"

"No – I don't know… I thought I had, but I'm sure I was mistaken," she said, trying desperately not to stammer.

She tried desperately to believe it had not been Morgan. *Her* Morgan, with the persuasive, silvery Welsh tongue, who had taught her the ways of love, and who could not possibly betray her like that…

She swallowed convulsively. It couldn't have been him. It was a trick of the light. Or perhaps everyone she saw resembled him simply because she longed to see him so much. Perhaps she heard an echo of him in every other man's voice because she longed to hear him whispering in her ear.

It was a known fact, according to a book she had read, that the mind could play strange tricks, conjuring up the beloved's face even when it was impossible for him to be in the place where you imagined it. Or something. It was why widows often imagined they saw their dead husbands smiling at them from the foot of their beds, when it was no more than an illusion borne out of loneliness and grief. She found herself reciting the ponderous words in her head as she tried to bolster up her confidence and belief in her beloved.

"You do look a bit odd, Immy." She heard Daisy's voice penetrate her whirling thoughts. "Perhaps we should go home and see if Daddy's had anymore thoughts on your idea."

Imogen tried to remember how disastrous their family situation was, but for the life of her, her own prospects kept getting in the way. Or, more likely, the lack of them. Morgan had never said anything about marriage, but she had assumed it was what he intended eventually, when her father decided she was old enough. Now she wasn't so sure.

She would rather think of *anything* but the sickening thought that Morgan was actually seeing someone else. But she couldn't divert her thoughts from the image uppermost in her mind, especially remembering how he had teasingly hinted that he was going to give her a very special gift for her birthday.

"It will have to be something fairly insignificant," she had teased him back. "I can't show off anything too brazenly, since my family don't know anything about you!"

It had been their lovely secret, and she had imagined a ring, or a locket, or some other token of love. Now, the idea of any gift at all seemed like a mockery. And she knew she must find out for sure if she had really seen him.

She couldn't bear to doubt him like this. Like her father, it had always been her way to face trouble head on. She stopped walking suddenly.

"I've just remembered that I said I might call on Helen Church this afternoon. It had quite slipped my mind with all that Father told us. She hasn't been well lately, so you two go on home and I'll be back at teatime."

"I don't know why you bother with her," Daisy said. "She's such a simpleton, and her brother's always bragging about joining the army, as if he's going to conquer the world if another war comes. I'm sure he *wants* it to happen just so he can become a hero!"

"I bother about her because she's my friend. And James Church has his head screwed on properly, Daisy. There's plenty of talk about another war in some circles."

"Well, I don't want to hear it," Daisy said. "Cook has too many gory tales to tell about the last one for anybody daft enough to listen to them."

"Don't waste your breath arguing with her, Immy," Elsie advised. "You go and visit Helen and give her my love."

Immy watched them go, bright in their summer frocks, Elsie no doubt admonishing Daisy about her flippant attitude to anything serious. But that was Daisy, Immy thought, with a rush of affection for her youngest sister.

And maybe it was no bad thing to be able to flit through life.

Her thoughts switched at once, knowing she was only going to make a token visit to her friend Helen, confined to bed with a sore throat for the past week.

Her first mission was to speed through the streets leading away from Welsh Back to see if she could catch another glimpse of Morgan and the girl he was with. Because, she realised as her heart gave an uncomfortable little leap, she was becoming more and more certain that she hadn't been mistaken at all.

–

Helen Church was sitting in the small summerhouse in her scented back garden when her mother called out that she had a visitor. She looked up from the book she was reading, and her pretty face creased into a delighted smile as she saw her friend Imogen coming towards her. She stretched out her manicured hand in welcome.

"Immy, how lovely! I've been so out of touch since I've had this wretched sore throat. I think everyone was too afraid of catching it to come near me."

"I'm sure that's not true," Immy said with a laugh. "But are you quite well now? And should you be outside?"

"Oh, pooh, of course I should! It's summer, isn't it? Come and sit with me, and when Mother's brought us out some lemonade, you can tell me all your news."

Her mother was nothing if not predictable, and minutes later a jug of fresh lemonade and two glasses were duly delivered on a tray, and Mrs Church was warmly enquiring after Immy's mother.

"As well as is reasonable to expect, Mrs Church. We can't really hope for more," Immy replied noncommittally, praying that she wouldn't continue with questions about the family. She wasn't ready yet to confide in anyone except Helen about how bad things were looking. Helen was the one who shared her secrets. The only one who knew anything about Morgan.

Immy had begun to realise that the shock of her father's news hadn't fully sunk in yet, and the vague plans for the future were no more than clutching at straws to try to make things seem less horrendous than they were.

Besides, Helen's family was more well to do than her own, she thought uneasily. Mrs Church was a distant relative of the nobility, however far down the scale – and Immy wasn't too sure how she would feel about her daughter's best friend contemplating taking in lodgers.

Being in trade was perfectly respectable nowadays, of course, especially when it was a family affair, but being obliged to take in lodgers was entirely different…and until this very moment, it had never occurred to her before.

"So are you going to tell me what's wrong, Immy darling?" she heard Helen's voice say gently, when her mother had left them alone. "I can see there's something troubling you. It's not – you haven't had a falling-out with MR, have you?"

She always used his initials, since it made the secret they shared seem more delicious.

"I almost wish it was something as simple as that," Immy muttered. "A falling-out can always be put right. In fact it only has a *little* bit to do with him."

"*What*, then? Goodness, don't keep me in suspense, Immy! What's happened to upset you? Has he said something – or done something?"

"No, and I dare say I'm just being silly. I imagined I saw him walking out with someone else earlier this afternoon, that's all. I'm still not sure if it was him, but it makes my stomach churn whenever I think of it."

"Well, you goose, you'll just have to ask him, won't you? But from the way you talk about him, I can't imagine he thinks of any other girl but you. I'm sure it wasn't him you saw."

"Perhaps you're right. I certainly *want* to believe it."

Immy took a long draught of lemonade, her eyes clouded, still certain it *had* been Morgan she had seen, and not at all sure how you went about tackling a young man to find out if he was two-timing you. That was the current expression used by all the Hollywood film stars, wasn't it? Two-timing. It sounded glamorous and sophisticated enough on the silver screen, but in real life it was just sordid and ugly.

And in a moment, it seemed, the sight of Morgan – if it had been him, for she had been unable to catch up with the couple and confirm her suspicion – had turned her from her usual confident, practical self, with a far more romantic and sensual streak than anyone else knew, into a mass of insecurity.

"So what else is it?" Helen persisted. "Immy, I hate to see you looking so unhappy. Is your mother worse – or has that idiot Baz rattled your father again with his talk of going to sea, or whatever his latest idea is?"

"We're losing the shop," Immy said abruptly.

Helen sat back, pushing a hand through her fashionably waved fair hair. A look that was almost bewilderment widened her blue eyes.

Like her mother, she was involved in charity work and committees, and had no need for a regular job. Her father, Gordon Church, was a prominent solicitor, and her brother James, just down from university, had a well mapped-out career in the army ahead of him. They were a world away from a family business in haberdashery, and Immy had never felt it more acutely than she did at that moment.

"What do you mean, you're losing the shop? Where is it going, then?" Helen asked, with a feeble attempt at humour.

"It's serious, Helen, and please keep all that I'm about to tell you to yourself, at least for the time being."

"I'm sorry, darling. And of course I'll say nothing. But I don't understand, so please won't you explain?" Helen asked more humbly.

Imogen drew a deep breath, knowing she had to say it all in a rush, because if she didn't she would probably dissolve into tears. "A big northern company is buying out the entire row of shops, and since we're only leaseholders of Caldwell's Supplies we don't have a say in it. Apparently, we're in some kind of debt as well, and my father wants us to move to a smaller house, but we all know how Mother would hate it and that it would upset her terribly, so I've suggested we take in paying guests, and my father's mulling over the idea right now, and I know you'll think it's an awful thing to have to do—"

"Why on earth should I?" Helen's voice held genuine astonishment and more than a hint of indignation. "Do you think I'm such a snob, Immy? I think it's a brave and beautiful thing to suggest, and your father should be very proud to have a daughter like you who can turn thoughts of disaster into hope the way you always do."

"Good Lord, do I?" Immy said with a wobbly smile. "I told Elsie not to make me sound like a saint, and now you're doing it too."

"Well, there you are then. We all think the world of you – and so does MR, I'm sure."

"Perhaps," Immy said, plunging farther into depression, and wishing she'd never said anything at all. But she'd had to tell someone or burst. And Helen was her dearest friend, the one she could rely on to support her in whatever she did.

"You won't think badly of me if I have to kowtow to strangers living in the house, then?" she went on, demeaning herself still more.

"Immy, the day you kowtow to anyone will be the day the moon turns blue," Helen said. "And as for the other matter – well, if MR turns out to be a rat, you can always marry James, and then we'll truly be sisters, won't we?"

Immy laughed hesitantly – for the first time in ages, it seemed. "I'm sure James wouldn't want to marry *me*!"

"Wouldn't he? Oh, well, I've got my own thoughts on that," Helen said airily. "But you can test the water for yourself. He's due home from seeing his pals any time now."

Immy felt a momentary panic at this new idea on top of all her other worries. "I'd better go, then. I don't want him to see me looking such a mess."

"You look perfectly lovely. And for goodness' sake, sit down again. I've never seen you so jumpy, and I'm sure you need to calm down before you go home and face the family."

Immy bit her lip. Helen was always calm, but then she had nothing in her life to ruffle her. Everything went along swimmingly, and no doubt in time she would make a wonderful marriage to a wonderful man and they would go on to have wonderful, well-behaved children…

"Immy Caldwell, if I'm not mistaken! By all that's wonderful, it's good to see you!"

Immy began laughing again as James Church swept into sight, tall and handsome, fair haired and blue eyed like his sister. She laughed up into his eyes, and felt her heart miss a small beat as she saw the warmth of his expression. She hadn't seen him for some months, and he had broadened in that time. If she hadn't been so head-over-heels in love with Morgan…

"It's good to see you too, James. How goes it?"

"Very well," he said, sprawling easily on another chair. "I'm joining my regiment in a month's time, and the outlook is exciting, if you know what I mean."

Helen groaned. "Don't start him on the topic of war, Immy. He's convinced it's coming, and we're never going to hear the end of it from him."

"Of course it's coming," he told her. "Why do you think the ARP service was formed last year if the government doesn't expect air raids in the future? And now they've ordered a thousand new Spitfire fighters to be built. They're not going to waste taxpayers' money on war machines unless they expect them to be used."

"Stop it, James. You're making me nervous," Helen said.

"So you should be. If Hitler decides to ride roughshod over Europe, we'll all be involved. We can't let him get away with it. Even you, my sweet, will find yourself having to buckle down and do some war work, even if it's only dispensing tea and sympathy at a military canteen."

"I'd be capable of more than that! Not that I think it will happen – and neither do you, do you, Immy?"

"We-ell, I suppose there has to be a reason why people are starting to move out of London to the country, and the wireless reports are always so gloomy," Imogen admitted, shivering.

"Oh, *them*!" Helen dismissed them scathingly. "Those wireless people would have you believe we were all going to be bombed in our beds at any minute."

"Or in our shelters. I know my father's starting to think they might need to build them," Immy pointed out, half wishing this conversation hadn't got so serious, but thankful it had taken her mind off her own troubles for the moment.

"There speaks a girl with foresight," James said approvingly. "So what will you do in the war, Immy? I rather fancy you as a nurse, soothing my fevered brow."

She grimaced. "Now you are tempting fate – and you shouldn't do it. I'm not sure I could be a nurse, anyway."

Helen had obviously been thinking about people from London being sent to the country for safety.

"We'd be quite safe here, though, wouldn't we? I mean, we're such a long way away from London. I'm sure life would go on just the same for us."

"Helen, sweetie, sometimes I think you live in a world of your own. If you bothered to read the newspapers, you would know that the government is taking Hitler's threat very seriously indeed. If – *when* – war comes, life will never be the same again for any of us, and this will be a war of the air far more than the last one was. I'd say Bristol will be a prime target for bombing, with the docks and the aircraft industry. Nowhere will be safe this time."

Helen jumped up, her eyes full of distress now.

"You're being horrid and you're frightening us, James. Immy and I aren't going to listen to any more of it. We're going indoors to play some gramophone records and leave you to your beastly old war fantasies."

"All right. But they're not fantasies, Helen, and pretty soon you'll have to believe it."

He caught hold of Immy's hand as she made to follow her friend. "You know I wouldn't scare you for the world, Immy. But I believe in being realistic, and I thought you would understand."

"I do," she said. "I think I'm beginning to understand only too well."

Before this afternoon she had never contemplated Bristol becoming such a target. And here, today, on this beautiful August afternoon, she didn't want to visualise the skies darkening with enemy planes. It was hard to imagine an enemy coming out of the blue, intent on killing people, or even that Germans could be their enemies again. The war to end all wars was long over…but perhaps clinging to such a belief was no more than living in a kind of fool's paradise.

She stayed a while longer, since Helen was clearly upset at James's predictions, and when she left she promised to come again the following week and report progress.

"And you be sure to tackle MR if you have any real doubts," Helen whispered as they said their goodbyes. "But I honestly don't think you've anything to worry about there, darling. I hope things go well on the family front, though."

They hugged one another, and Immy made her way back home, thinking how breezily life went by for Helen. She had never consciously envied her, but right then she thought it must be lovely not to have to worry a jot about money.

Until this afternoon, when it all seemed in danger of disappearing, it had simply never occurred to her to wonder how her father had ever managed to support a family and a large house with domestic staff all these years. But it occurred to her now.

Chapter Three

Imogen's mind was full of questions she had never thought about before, because there had been no need to question anything. Five years ago, when Teddy had been born and her mother had been so near to death after his traumatic birth, she had been only fourteen, and the others had been even younger. They were well-loved children who had been brought up with the old values of being seen and not heard, especially where adult matters were concerned.

But she was no longer a child, she thought resentfully. She would be twenty in a month's time, and she had already known another kind of love, however innocent compared with some of the sizzling kisses seen at the picture houses.

She bit her lip, remembering how Helen had once asked her, wide-eyed, if they had gone *all the way*…and she had answered crossly that of course they hadn't. Only a *little* bit of the way in reality, and it had seemed daring and a bit frightening when Morgan had begged to be allowed to slide his hand inside her blouse, and she had hesitantly agreed with red-faced embarrassment and a throbbing heart.

Nice girls didn't go all the way. *Really* nice girls never allowed more than a kiss and a cuddle, despite what the more racy and glamorous stars of the silver screen might imply.

But today, thoughts of Morgan slipped in and out of her mind with less comfort than usual, and she applied herself to the more puzzling matter of how the family had survived even this long if things were so bad.

She racked her brains and vaguely recalled a conversation from long ago, when her mother had still been drawing in the audiences at the theatre, and Aunt Rose and Uncle Bertie had come to visit. She had crept to the top of the stairs in her nightgown as she heard the raised voices.

"You should curb it now, Quentin. Her place is at home looking after these children, not showing off her body to all and sundry. We all love her dearly, you know that, but it's not a seemly occupation for a wife and mother."

"I'd like to remind you that Frances is my wife, Rose. If she chooses to pursue her career and I agree to it, then it's our business, and nobody else's."

Imogen had heard her aunt's eloquent sniff. "Oh, well, of course, if she's bringing in the money—"

"That's not the reason, and you know it, Rose. I won't have you belittling me. Not that it's anything to do with you, but all our money is invested to support the business. With Father's legacy, I've put as much into it as Frances has, so I won't hear another thing about it."

Imogen hadn't heard anything more about it either, and it was a conversation she had virtually forgotten. Money had never been a topic of discussion. It had just been there, as necessary as wallpaper, but with no need for it to be mentioned.

But now perhaps it should be. Her heart skipped a beat, wondering what her father's reaction would be if she were to tackle him. It wasn't a daughter's place…but if she had been a son, no doubt he would have confided in her. Baz was far too young and scatter-brained to be told the facts, but she was not.

She walked up the hill to Vicarage Street, where they lived, seeing the tall houses through different eyes now. She loved their house, and so did her father. He had been born there, and so had all his children. It was cruel that they need even think of leaving it, Immy thought fiercely, especially on the whim of some greedy northern shopkeepers.

She found her father in his study, sitting motionless at his desk and staring into space. Her heart turned over, unable to bear seeing him like this.

"Daddy, won't you take me into your confidence?" she blurted out, with a catch in her throat.

He gave her a vague smile, ignoring her question. "Do you know how rarely you call me that, Immy?"

She took the bull by the horns. "That's not because I think any less of you. You know I love you and I always will. But I'm grown up now, and I think I deserve to know what's happening to us. I'll bet you've told Aunt Rose," she said with sudden intuition.

Quentin sighed. "I've always respected her opinion, even if I haven't always acted on it. I wanted her advice about sending Mother and Teddy to stay with her and Bertie, and since she always has to know every detail, it all came out about the possibility of selling the house."

"But *why*? It belongs to us, doesn't it? I know your parents left it to you, and surely there can't be so many debts that we can't continue to live here – and even start another small business somewhere else when Preston's takes over."

He sighed. "We can't afford to keep paying the people who are dependent on us, Immy. As for starting another shop, I simply can't invest money that may not be returned. Why Preston's even want to move down here in such troubled times, Lord only knows."

"I hadn't thought of that. Why would they want to move their business south, if what everybody says about another war is true?" She felt a glimmer of hope as her thoughts went off in a different direction. "So perhaps all the rumours mean nothing at all. At least we should be optimistic about that!"

She was trying to cheer him up, to emphasise the fact that she hated the entire Preston clan, whatever their intentions. She hated them with a passion for destroying her life. But, she realised, her father was looking at her sorrowfully now.

"Darling Immy, your loyalty is commendable, but I fear it's not Preston's who have ruined us. It's your father's ineptitude with money and bad investments, and you have no idea how it pains me to admit it to my child."

"I'm *not* a child," Immy almost wept. "Please confide in me, Daddy. I want to help."

"By suggesting that we take in lodgers, you mean?"

"Yes, if it means keeping us all together, and keeping the house we love. What's so wrong with it? Are we so proud that we can't change direction if needs must?"

He said nothing for a few minutes. "You've a wise head on young shoulders, Immy—"

She stamped her feet in annoyance. "Oh, how I wish people would stop telling me that! I'm being practical, that's all. I'm thinking of Mother, and all of us. I want to stay in Bristol, and so do the others, Daisy and Baz especially. We certainly don't want to move down to Weston and live with Aunt Rose!"

"Would that be so awful?"

She stared at him. "I suppose you're thinking about that old war again. I sometimes think men are obsessed with the idea. James Church was prattling on about it earlier today. I think he *wants* another war!"

"I doubt that, but having been in the last lot, I can see his reasoning, darling. If he's set on joining the army, as you say, then he'll want to justify himself. You don't become a soldier to twiddle your thumbs and go on endless parades."

"We're getting off the point, aren't we?" Immy said, even though she knew she had started it. "Are we going to think about my guest-house idea or not?"

She was taking the initiative far more than ever before, but in a weird way she felt more like the parent, and he the child right now. He looked so uncertain, so beaten, and she had to do all she could to bring back the smile to his face.

"We'll think about it," he said. "But I still think your mother will be best off in the country, and Teddy too. And since it upsets you, I won't mention the reason why."

"And Miss Lindsey? Does she have to go?"

"She has already packed her bags and gone," Quentin said.

Immy was astonished. But, like herself she supposed, when her father made up his mind, he acted on it.

"You might as well hear the rest of it", he continued. "I didn't want to tell you all the bad news in one fell swoop, but Preston's people will be moving down here very soon, and we have to be out of the shop in a month."

"My birthday will be very eventful this year, then, won't it?" Immy said bitterly.

"You'll still have your birthday tea and your aunt and uncle will come as usual. It will be a good time to discuss the future. For now I propose putting up sale posters in the shop next week to sell off the stock. Until we finally close, one or other of you girls will have to stay at home to look after your mother. You may draw up a rota as you wish."

"You *have* been doing some forward planning, then!" But she was more relieved than angry, because at least it seemed he was thinking more positively than before.

"Darling girl, do you think I would have wished all this to happen?" he said suddenly. "I don't intend to tell you the details, but I trusted people to deal with our investments, and it all went wrong. But at least we still have each other. As long as we still have the family, we'll be all right."

She ran around the desk and threw her arms around him.

"Of course we do. We always will, and that's what makes us strong, isn't it?"

Considering she felt as helpless a baby, she wasn't at all sure of her own words, but she felt his answering hug, and knew she had said the right thing. Then they both jumped, startled, as the door opened, and Frances wandered in.

"I can't find Miss Lindsey anywhere," she complained. "She always reads to Teddy and me before teatime, and he's getting very cross."

Quentin spoke steadily, knowing that lies would be kinder. "Remember I told you about Miss Lindsey's sister who's very ill, my love? I'm afraid Miss Lindsey has had to go and look after her, and she may have to stay for quite a while."

"Will she?" said Frances, staring. "What will happen to Teddy and me, then?"

Immy felt her heart wrench. Where was all the vibrant passion her mother had displayed on the stage, the reaching out to the audiences that had made them adore her so much? Until that moment she hadn't realised quite how introverted Frances had become, with all the self-centredness of the semi-invalid. But perhaps it was better so. Teddy would display the tantrums, but not her mother.

"I'll come and read to you both, Mother," she said swiftly. "Would you like that?"

"Would you, dear?" Frances said in delight. "How lovely!"

Without a backward glance at her father, Immy took her mother's hand and guided her out of the study and upstairs to the nursery, where Teddy sat on a stool glowering.

"Where's Lindy?" he said, using his own name for the nurse-companion.

Immy answered him brightly, knowing what to expect. "She's had to go away for a while, Teddy, so I'm going to read to you and Mother today."

"I don't want you! I want Lindy!" he shouted, kicking out just as Immy neared to him, searing her shins.

"You little brat," she hissed at him. "You'll have me and like it." She would not normally have spoken to harshly, but the events of today had stretched her patience to breaking point.

"Tell her, Mama," he shrieked, clutching at Frances's skirt. He was a beautiful child, but right now Immy thought him the work of the devil.

But Frances seemed quite unconcerned as Teddy clutched at her skirt. She pulled him on to her lap on her rocking chair and hummed softly, crooning to him and smoothing the hair from his angry little forehead.

"Hush now, baby," she told him. "We'll listen to Immy's story and then we'll have some tea."

They were like something out of a fairy story themselves, thought Immy. *And who knows what's to become of them…?* She turned away, her thoughts in torment, and opened the book Miss Lindsey had been reading to them.

–

Elsie Caldwell was the quiet one of the family, but that didn't mean she wasn't deep. She had little patience with Daisy's wild ideas; she knew enough to keep her thoughts to herself until she felt the need to speak out.

Daisy's reckless ambition to follow in her mother's footsteps would almost certainly come to nothing in Elsie's opinion, and when it did, she would be ready to lend a sympathetic ear. But performing on the stage in front of masses of strangers, and risking their displeasure if they didn't like you, was completely alien to Elsie's nature.

She much preferred to remain behind the scenes in whatever she did. She was quite happy to spend her time in the back room of the shop with her needle and her sewing machine and her flat iron and take in the repairs and produce the neat stitching for which she was praised.

She was happiest when a lady brought in a hat that needed renovating or bought some silks and buckram from the shop with only a vague idea of a hat to be made for a special occasion, leaving Elsie herself to design and produce it. She had a skill that she didn't want to abandon, and the events of the afternoon had made her think more seriously about it than ever before.

"What are you thinking about, Elsie?" she heard Daisy say crossly, as they sat on their deckchairs underneath the apple tree in the small back garden. "Nobody talks to me. Immy's disappeared to see that friend of hers, and you look as if you're somewhere in dreamland."

"Immy came back a while ago. And if I look as if I'm in dreamland, it's because I am. We'll all have to pull our weight in the future, so I'm thinking about what to do, and not considering silly ideas, either."

"You all think I'm silly, don't you?"

"No, we don't. Just young and a bit headstrong at times, perhaps." Before Daisy could snap back at her, Elsie put her hand over her sister's and squeezed it. "We all have to be sensible now, Daisy, and take what Daddy told us seriously."

"Yes, ma'am," Daisy muttered. "So what great plan have you got in mind?"

Elsie took a deep breath. "Even if Daddy agrees to this guest-house idea and we have to do our bit, I don't see why I can't continue with my sewing. I can still take in repairs, and I can still make hats, but I'll be doing it at home."

"Good Lord! And do you really think people will trail all the way up here to bring a torn jacket to be mended, or to ask you to create a Sunday hat?"

"Why not? They know my work."

"But they don't know Vicarage Street! Caldwell's Supplies is in the city, not in a hotchpotch of houses."

"Then I'll have to advertise," Elsie said, determined not to be defeated. "I'll get somebody to print me some leaflets and we'll put them on the shop counter, and I'll distribute some to houses and shops as well."

"We don't know anybody who can print leaflets."

"I do," a voice said behind them.

They turned at once, not having heard Imogen come out to the garden, exhausted after reading for an hour, and having Teddy fall asleep in the middle of it. Frances was dozing as well now, however, and she was glad of a welcome breath of fresh air.

"Did you hear what we were talking about?" Elsie asked.

"Yes, and I think it's a splendid idea. But you're quite right. You will need to advertise, otherwise people won't know you intend to continue with your sewing."

"Who do you know then, Immy?" Daisy said curiously.

"A young man who works in the print room of the local newspaper," Immy said evenly. "I only know him slightly, but I'm sure if I asked him he'd be able to do some leaflets for a reasonable fee."

"Is he your young man?" Daisy said immediately. "If he is, I'll bet Daddy doesn't know anything about it."

"He's just someone I met," Immy retorted, feeling an absolute traitor to the love of her life, but with no intention of letting this bright-eyed little madam know anything about Morgan. Not yet, anyway.

"Will he do it, do you think?" Elsie said. "I couldn't afford to pay much, but it would take ages to do them by hand myself, and it would be far more professional if they were printed. Unless you'd care to type them all out, Immy?"

She shook her head. "That would take ages too. I'll have to ask my friend the next time I see him. I think

47

Father will have a job for you to do soon, though, Elsie. He wants some posters for the shop window to say we're having a sale" – she swallowed before she went on, because it still seemed so unreal – "and that the shop will be closing at the end of September."

"*What?* So soon?" Elsie and Daisy exclaimed simultaneously.

"I'm afraid so. I don't know any more details; you'll have to discuss the design of the poster with him, Elsie."

"I'll do it now," she said, already considering the way it should appear in order to attract customers. Despite her dismay she knew they all had to move on, and it was becoming increasingly obvious that the change to their lives was to be swift.

"Who's your young man, Immy?" Daisy enquired when Elsie had left them.

"Nobody you know, and he's not my young man. Why don't you go and help Cook get tea ready? We all have to pull our weight now, so you might as well get used to it, Daisy."

Her sister scowled, as belligerent as Teddy, but since Immy had sat down on the vacant deck-chair and closed her eyes against the sun's glare, Daisy knew she would get nothing more out of her, and she went indoors, banging the door behind her.

By now Immy was more concerned with what she was going to say to Morgan than bothering about Daisy's flashes of temper. The shock of seeing him with his arm so blatantly around another girl in the middle of town on a Sunday afternoon was receding a little now, and she was persuading herself that it probably hadn't been him at all.

She didn't *want* to believe it had been him, and the moment she confronted him and put it into words, the more real it would become. It wasn't like her to take the coward's way out...but this time, she thought weakly, just this once, it might be the more prudent way.

Besides, what would she do if he denied it? She would have to believe him, of course, but it would put a blight on their relationship, because he would think she didn't trust him. And if he admitted it, it would all be over anyway.

Because of their close, rather cloistered family life, Immy had never had a young man before, and she didn't know the right way to handle this situation at all. If she dared, she would write to one of those "Aunt Em" pages in one of the women's magazines and ask for advice.

But she couldn't have a formal letter sent back to the house without questions being asked, and she might have to wait weeks or months for a reply to appear in print. And she didn't have that kind of patience. Better not to know at all, she decided, than to be disillusioned.

She only saw Morgan on Wednesday afternoons when the shop closed for half a day, and it seemed an age to wait. Before then, her father had been in further consultation with the accountant and the landlord, and had meetings with people they didn't know, whose outcome he kept to himself. They still hadn't come to any decision about the house.

Everyone had become so gloomy over the last few days, and with the sale posters in the shop window now, customers were asking questions they hardly knew how to answer. At home, Teddy was at his worst, and their mother's incessant humming and lack of concern about the presence of her so-called "dearest companion" had begun to unnerve them all.

If Frances could be so uncaring about Miss Lindsey, would she feel any more loss when parted from any of her family? It was an alarming thought, and one which underlined her rapid decline. Was keeping this house so important after all? It was only a building. Immy began to wish she had never mentioned the paying guests at all.

–

Early on Tuesday evening they received an unexpected visit from Quentin's sister and brother-in-law. Their battered old Morris car drew up in the road outside the house soon after they had all finished tea.

By the time the rest of them had washed their hands and assembled in the sitting-room for the obligatory quizzing, the couple were ensconced with Frances and Teddy. They were clearly desperate to give up trying to make intelligent conversation with either of them, however.

Baz had disappeared as soon as the shop closed. He still wasn't home, and Immy knew her father would have words with him when he deigned to join them.

"We've come to stay for a night or two – if you'll have us, Quentin – and to try to make sense of what's happening," Rose announced, after a brief kiss on her brother's cheek.

Immy glanced at her sisters. It was just as she had suspected: even before they had been given the news, Aunt Rose and Uncle Bertie had been acquainted with it. Treating them like children, she fumed, when they had every right to know first…

"If my mother had seen me frown like that, Imogen," she heard Aunt Rose say tartly, "she would have told me my face would stay like it."

Well, yours didn't, Immy said silently, praying she hadn't spoken the words aloud as she forced a smile to her lips.

"How are you, Aunt Rose?" she said dutifully.

"Well enough, my girl, or would be, if I didn't have all of you to worry about."

Immy glanced at Elsie again, sitting there with her eyes downcast. Elsie didn't say much, but privately they all thought Aunt Rose a bit of a tartar. They knew very well how deeply she cared for them all, however.

"Did you bring me anything, Auntie?" Teddy said, young enough to be oblivious to undercurrents.

His aunt laughed. "Now what could I possibly bring a lovely boy like you?"

"Weston rock," he said hopefully, at which Uncle Bertie guffawed as if he'd said something terribly witty and produced a paper bag containing five pink sticks of rock, like a conjurer bringing them out of a hat.

They all said thank you, although none of the girls cared for the stuff anymore. It was only the boys who thought it a treat. Privately, Immy thought it was nasty, and sticky, and just what you expected from a seaside town noted for its donkey rides and ice-cream stands. Not that she had ever minded *those*, she thought, remembering their childhood outings to the sea.

"So what have you decided to do about the house?" Bertie added his weight to his wife's question.

They were both in their fifties, rotund and grey haired, each as bickeringly argumentative as the other, simply because it was their way. And since they were childless, they had taken it upon themselves to be pseudo-caretakers of this large family.

"Take in paying guests, probably," Quentin said, having no stomach for a lengthy discussion when he was tired, and ignoring the gasps of his three daughters.

"Sensible," Rose said. "I wouldn't want to see our parents' house sold to any old Tom, Dick or Harry."

"I thought you'd object, Aunt Rose," Immy said.

"Did you? Then perhaps you don't know me as well as you thought you did, girl. There's ample room here to take in at least three or four, though I suggest you advertise carefully for suitable guests."

"Where's the other boy?" Uncle Bertie said suddenly.

As if on cue, Baz sidled into the room, mumbling apologies for being late. He stayed at the back of the room, perched on a chair, as if preferring to make himself invisible, which was unusual in itself.

"Immy knows somebody who can print leaflets," Daisy said slyly. "He's going to advertise Elsie's hat-making."

Immy felt her face go as hot as fire, and Elsie rounded on her sister at once.

"Nothing's been decided yet—"

"What's all this?" Quentin said.

Elsie spoke quickly. "I thought I'd be able to carry on with my sewing at home, once we give up the shop. That is all right, isn't it?"

"It's admirable, Elsie," he told her. "And who is this person who's going to print the leaflets, Immy?"

"I haven't approached him yet," Immy said, wishing Daisy to Kingdom Come for putting her in this position. "It's just someone I met who's in the printing business."

"A decent fellow, I hope," Aunt Rose said.

From the back of the room Baz gave a sudden snigger, and everyone turned to look at him. Immy's eyes widened imperceptibly. What did the little snitch know? And more importantly, what would he tell?

"Do you have something to say, Baz?" his father enquired.

He shook his head and Immy breathed more easily. She wouldn't put anything past him. He was becoming far too big for his boots…Even as the words entered her head, she found herself looking at his feet, and at the footwear he polished on Quentin's orders every night before he went to bed, the same as they all did.

Today Baz's boots were scuffed and muddy, no matter how he tried to hide them beneath his chair. And when she looked at him more keenly, she could see there were bruises on his cheek that were just starting to discolour. They had all been so wrapped up in the discussion of the moment, and Aunt Rose's domineering presence, that none of them had noticed it before. And from the look of him, Baz was desperately hoping no one would notice it now, and wishing he hadn't brought attention to himself. But it was too late.

"Good Lord, look at the boy! Have you been fighting and disgracing the family name?" Aunt Rose demanded.

Quentin stared at his son hard. His family was his pride and joy, and although it was his right to censure and chastise them when the need arose, he objected strongly to anyone else doing it – especially his sister, who had no idea what it was like to bring up a family at all. But this matter clearly needed investigating.

"Out with it, Baz. What do you mean by coming home looking like a hooligan?"

Baz nervously wiped the back of his hand across his nose, and they all saw the faint trickle of blood on his sleeve.

"He's running wild," Aunt Rose snapped. "Look at him. A fine state he'll be in tomorrow behind the shop counter. The customers will think they've come to a zoo."

Big and boisterous as he was, Baz knew better than to defy his father, at least most of the time. But right now, he felt as small as a pea. And his aunt, whom he'd always thought had a soft spot for him, was glaring at him.

He jumped up from his chair, his hands clenched at his sides, no matter how it stretched the skin of his knuckles and made them smart where they had connected with a couple of the young thugs at the waterfront.

"I don't want to stand behind a stupid shop counter tomorrow, or any other day, if you must know," he shouted in a rage. "I'm fed up with being called a sissy. Old Enoch Bray has offered me a job on his ferry-boat if I want it, and I've said yes, so there!"

All fourteen years and eight stone of him was bristle and fire at that moment. His eyes burned with the tears he wouldn't shed, his ribs ached from the kicks he'd endured, and his cheeks felt stiff and swollen from where those illiterate bastards had jeered at him and punched him. Well, he wasn't having any more of it. He was as good as them – *better* than them – and it was because he thought that way that he'd got into the fight in the first place.

He waited for the explosion. Instead he heard a slow hand-clap and gaped in astonishment at his Uncle Bertie.

"I always thought it a namby-pamby job for a young man with your abilities," he said. "I reckon you could go far as a boxer, boy."

Baz flinched as his father voiced a rare expletive beneath his breath.

"I don't want to be a stupid boxer," he almost shrieked. "I just want to be a ferryman and work on the river."

"You might as well let the boy do what he wants, Quentin," Rose put in. "He's obviously not cut out to be a shopkeeper. I always told you so."

Quentin threw up his hands. "Has my entire family now decided to dictate to me what's right?"

"Well, you don't seem to be making too good a job of overseeing things, do you?" Rose – the only one who dared to voice the words – remarked.

Her words stunned them all into momentary silence. The girls looked nervous and anxious, and in the corner of the room, Teddy was snivelling, sucking on his stick of rock and plastering it all over Frances's frock. She didn't seem to notice, however, and continued to smile at them all and hum beneath her breath.

Bertie cleared his throat. "Why don't we get down to brass tacks instead of all this arguing?"

"That's rich, coming from you," Quentin snarled.

Bertie went on as if he hadn't spoken. "What we've actually come here to say, Quentin, is that we'd like to take Teddy off your hands for a while. No ifs or buts. If this house is to be overrun with strangers the child will be lost in the crush."

"No child of mine would ever be treated in that way!"

"Listen to what Bertie says, Quentin, dear," Rose said, her hand on his arm, her voice softer than usual. "We all know that Frances can't go on like this forever, and sooner or later you'll need to do what Doctor Wolfe says, and send her somewhere where she can be properly looked after. You have your affairs to sort out, and the rest of the children are growing up fast, but Teddy is still a baby."

"I'm not a baby!" he shouted, burying his face in Frances's skirt again.

"We know you're not, old chap," Bertie said, kneeling beside him now so that they were on the same eye level. "But Auntie Rose and me don't have any children, so we'd like to borrow you for a while. You and me could go for walks on the beach every day, and we could go fishing in the river. We're going to buy a dog, and you could think of a name for him. He could be your dog if you lived with us, Teddy. What do you say?"

I'd say you should have been a diplomat, thought Immy.

Chapter Four

Imogen had longed for and dreaded the thought of Wednesday in equal measure. The grassy hill where she and Morgan always met wasn't far above Vicarage Street, though well away from the tell-tale windows of any houses.

She was as eager as ever to see him, but today was different. There were so many things she had to tell him, yet so much more that she couldn't bear to say.

As always, her heartbeat quickened when she saw him approach, though today it was thumping to a different rhythm.

"How's my best girl?" he said in his lilting Welsh voice, his arms reaching out to encircle her slim waist while he pressed his mouth possessively on to hers.

She breathed in the freshness of soap on his skin, and no matter how hard she tried to not let it affect her, she felt her eyes mist over. His *best* girl? When she had so hoped and prayed and believed that she was his *only* girl? But they were just words, she told herself. They meant nothing.

Nevertheless, she couldn't help standing stiffly in his arms. She normally melted into them, and he sensed the difference at once. He held her away from him, his dark eyes puzzled, his black curly hair ruffled by the small breeze on the hilltop.

"What's wrong, sweetie?"

She blurted it out at once. "We're losing the shop."

"I know."

She stared up at him. "You *know*? How do you know?"

"It's news. Preston's Emporium have instructed us to place advertisements in the newspaper in a couple of weeks' time. The whole row of little shops will be closed for the week, while Preston's move in their stock and erect new shop signs. It's the way big business works, see? It will be an impressive place when it's all under one banner, and it'll put that corner of Bristol on the map."

She felt betrayed by his words and the enthusiasm with which he spoke them. Calling their shop a *little* shop, when her father had worked so hard to build it up! Her face burned with humiliation. He was being so insensitive! Didn't he know what this was doing to them? Was he so blind that he couldn't see how this must be affecting her whole family? The shop was their livelihood!

"Anyway, we don't want to waste time talking about old shops, do we?" Morgan went on, oblivious to her churning thoughts. "Let's find our special place and have a cuddle and make the most of the afternoon."

She swallowed hard. "Can't you appreciate my feelings about what's happening?"

He shrugged. "It's making a packet for your old man, I dare say, so I can't see why it's such a bad thing... Oh, come on, darling, don't be so touchy."

"*Touchy!* I'm devastated, if you must know. And not that it's any of your business, but we don't actually *own* the shop. I don't know the details, and I wouldn't tell you if I did, but my father's upset, and none of us knows what's happening anymore. We're even thinking of taking in *lodgers*" — she emphasised the less attractive name, since she was starting to feel so wretched – "and we'll all have to do something else, and my little brother's probably going to live with my aunt and uncle at the seaside—"

"Taking in lodgers, eh? Well, how about me, for a start? I could come creeping to your room at night…"

As Immy pushed him violently away, he began to get angry.

"Oh, for God's sake, Immy, I'm only teasing. Put a smile on your face, can't you? You know I can't stand seeing you glum like this."

"I know that. You expect me to be always sweet and responsive, don't you? Is that how you like all your young ladies to be, Morgan?"

She was breathing heavily now, and so was he.

"What do you mean by that?"

"I saw you out walking on Sunday afternoon, in Welsh Back," she accused. "It *was* you, wasn't it?"

Her teeth were threatening to chatter, but she wouldn't give him the satisfaction of letting him see how upset she was. Because of course it had been him, and she had always known it, no matter how much she had tried to deny it.

He didn't deny it either. "What if it was? She's a work colleague, that's all. I do have other friends, Immy, and so should you. You shouldn't always be clinging to those sisters of yours and never see anybody else."

"I have other friends too, thank you. And do you always walk around town in broad daylight with your arm around a work colleague?" she went on, seemingly unable to stop.

"I didn't know you could be such a shrew, Imogen."

"I'm not," she said, choked. "I just thought I was your girl, that's all."

"You are," he said, putting his arms around her again. "Really you are. Catherine's just somebody at work."

"I see. And if you'd *happened* to meet me on Sunday afternoon, would you have told her I was just somebody who works in a shop on Blackboy Hill?"

"Probably. Since you're the one who's been insisting all this time that we keep things secret, what else would you have had me say? You're the one who says we can only see each other one afternoon a week, and hell's teeth, Immy, I'm not a monk!"

He certainly wasn't. Even now, she could feel herself weakening as his fingers stroked the soft inner flesh of her arms. He was slowly leading her to their favourite hollow, pulling her gently down beside him, and his kiss was very tender on her lips. And she did love him...didn't she?

"You know what those damn cobbles are like on those soft-soled shoes you ladies wear," he was whispering now. "Catherine was in danger of tripping, and you must have caught sight of me when I was trying to keep her upright, that's all. I'd only bumped into her by accident, anyway."

Oh, he was so plausible – and Immy truly didn't want to lose him...not when everything else in her life seemed to be slipping away. Foolish or not, at least she could still hold on to this...

It suddenly dawned on her that his hand had slid around to the front of her bodice and was fondling the soft mound of her breast.

She captured it there for a moment longer, pressing it tightly to her in what was virtually a gesture of goodbye – except that he didn't know it – before wrenching it away.

"All right, but I'm not having any more of that today," she said in a clipped voice. "If you truly think anything of me, Morgan, you'll listen to me, because I've got something important to ask of you."

"Fire away," he said, his eyes narrowing.

She remembered her dream and was tempted to ask him if he could get her a typing position with the newspaper, so that she could work beside him. But even as she thought it, she knew she no longer wanted it. Not if the pretty Catherine also worked there. She would have to face her suspicions of them every single day and listen to his glib Welsh tongue telling her more lies.

Almost without noticing it, her feelings for him cooled several degrees at the thought. She *didn't* believe his story. She knew him for what he was, a charming flirt. Hadn't he charmed her in the first place? And did it really matter, when she had known in her heart of hearts that he was never going to be the marrying kind? Which was the only thing that really made a girl feel respectable.

"My sister Elsie is going to continue working at home," she said abruptly. "She's the clever one in the family as far as sewing is concerned, and she wants to advertise her skills. She needs some printed leaflets, Morgan, and I wondered if you could arrange to have them done for her. I've brought a rough idea to show you the wording she wants."

She fumbled in her bag for the piece of paper, not wanting him to guess how deflated she felt now at the way this day had deteriorated into a business arrangement, instead of returning the excitement of a clandestine meeting between lovers.

To her surprise, however, she was a little relieved as well. She had always sensed that Morgan's needs were going to become more demanding, and she had no intention of ever giving in to him. The residents of Vicarage Street were still shocked at the way a young girl in the vicinity had allowed herself to be seduced by a man. The young woman and her child had now been condemned to life in a lunatic asylum. It had happened at least ten years ago, and it still caused whispers and condemnation for the disgrace it had brought to her family.

Immy shivered. Nothing on earth would induce her to behave in such a way until she had a wedding ring on her finger. She thought she had been in love, but now she was just as sure that she wasn't. Not the steadfast kind of love her parents had, anyway, nor that of Aunt Rose and Uncle Bertie, whose marriage, despite their sometimes entertaining and blistering arguments, was rock solid.

"This wouldn't be any trouble," Morgan was saying now as he glanced at the piece of paper with Elsie's outlined wording. "I couldn't do it for nothing, of course—"

"Oh, we'd expect to pay you for your trouble, natur-ally," Immy said drily, thinking how grasping he sounded. "We couldn't afford much, though."

"You could always pay me in kind, sweetie," he said with a grin, and she squirmed away from him.

She had always liked his special endearment for her, but not anymore. It grated on her, and she wondered how she could ever have let herself fall for his smooth talking.

"No, I couldn't," she snapped. "And I don't think I want to see you again – except to arrange this business."

"Is this all because you saw me talking innocently to another girl? I didn't think you could be so narrow minded, but perhaps it's just as well I found out now!"

"Perhaps it is," she said, aware that her heart should be breaking, and knowing that actually it wasn't. It was almost a guilty feeling – and one that filled her with a little alarm – because it seemed to imply that she was as shallow as Morgan himself.

"So will you do the leaflets for Elsie?" she persisted, since it seemed to be the only thing they had to say to one another now.

"I dare say," he said coolly.

"That's not good enough. If you could get them done by next Wednesday, Elsie can start distributing them."

"No chance. Wednesday week or nothing. So how many?"

By the time they walked back down the hill, separately instead of giggling and snuggling together as usual, he had agreed to the price and number required. Immy held her head high as she went home to report to Elsie.

And a lone figure lifted his head out of the long grass, staring at his sister's stiffly retreating back, disappointed not to have seen anything more interesting to feed his vivid adolescent imagination.

—

Time didn't stand still just because the fabric of the Caldwells' lives were changing. If anything, it raced by at an ever-increasing and frightening speed. The shop remained open, the stock was being sold at highly discounted prices because Quentin would rather serve his faithful customers himself than sell on anything to the imperious Prestons.

Aunt Rose and Uncle Bertie decided to remain with them for a week, while Aunt Rose gave her expert advice on how to adapt the house to accommodate paying guests while retaining some family privacy.

By then, Teddy had become fully indoctrinated with the idea that he was going to live at the seaside for a while, where the sea was always blue, and the sands were always soft and warm for him and his new dog to romp on. Uncle

Bertie would take him fishing every day, and life would be one long blissful holiday.

"It almost makes me wish I were going too," Elsie said, hearing Teddy going on and on about it. "I'm sure Mother thinks she's going as well, though, from the way she keeps smiling and nodding at him. She's going to have an awful shock when she finds him not clinging to her anymore."

"I'm not so sure," Immy said. "Have you heard her mention Miss Lindsey this past week? I'm sure she's forgotten her existence already."

Elsie looked distressed. "I had the same feeling myself, Immy, and I can't bear it. It means that her mind's going much quicker than we thought." She hesitated. "I don't like to say this, but do you think Father should listen to what Doctor Wolfe says about sending her somewhere safe?"

"What can be safer than here, where we all love her?" Immy said fiercely. Then she sighed. "Oh, I know what you're saying, and we can't be her eyes and ears every minute of the day. She looks so pretty and normal when she walks about, as if she's a lady who's simply dreaming and taking the air. If she were to wander near the river, nobody would consider that she might be in danger."

"We must all watch her, then, and be sure she's never allowed to go out unsupervised."

Immy nodded slowly. "I know you're right, darling, but I feel so sad for her. She had the world at her feet, and now she's a virtual prisoner in her own home, isn't she?"

"But for her own safety," Elsie stressed. "And you must admit, we're the ones who are suffering on her account. *She* doesn't seem to suffer at all, and she's perfectly happy in her own world, restricted though it might be."

"I know, and we must all thank God for that."

Immy also thanked God that she had never confided anything about Morgan to Elsie and Daisy, especially not Daisy.

Morgan had come into the shop to show Elsie a dummy of her leaflet, and she had approved it at once. He had said he would deliver the finished articles when he could. It was so vague that it told Immy more clearly than words that their Wednesday-afternoon liaisons were well and truly over.

"He seems quite nice," Elsie remarked after he had gone. "Where did you meet him, Immy?"

"It was when the delivery boy failed to come with our newspaper and Father's trade magazine a few months ago, and I went to the offices myself to collect them," she explained.

"He's Welsh, isn't he?"

Immy suddenly realised her sister was showing a special interest in Morgan Raine, and that it must be curbed at once. And it had nothing to do with jealousy, she told herself fiercely.

"Yes, but don't let that lilting accent distract you. He already has a young lady, anyway."

And before Elsie could ask her how she knew that, she turned to smile at a new customer who had entered the shop.

"Good afternoon, sir," she said. "What can I do for you?"

He was tall and darkly good looking, and about the same age as Morgan, she guessed, which made him in his early twenties. But that was where the similarity ended, because this young man had a brooding look about him that reminded her sharply of Heathcliff in *Wuthering Heights*.

How absurd that was, to reach such an instant conclusion…but when he spoke, she realised she had been more intuitive than she knew.

"I'm not too sure about that, lass, but you can direct me to the proprietor of this establishment, if you would be so kind. You can give him my card, if you will, and tell him that Robert Preston's come to see him."

Immy's face flooded with colour, and she heard Elsie gasp beside her. Thankfully, Daisy was at home with Frances today, or she would no doubt have been toadying up to this film-starry character, no matter who he was.

"If it's my father you've come to see, I'm not so sure that he'll want to see you," she heard herself say freezingly. It was certainly no way to speak to a customer, let alone this man, but since Preston's were buying the entire building up, lock, stock and barrel, no matter what was said, she didn't bother to heed her words.

The man's eyes widened. They were very dark, flecked with hazel…and she had been reading too many romantic stories, Immy raged.

"So you're one of the daughters, are you? I heard they were a bonny bunch of lasses. And is this another one?" he enquired in his flat nasal tones, nodding towards Elsie.

The damned, insufferable gall of the man! Immy had hated anyone to do with Preston's sight unseen, and the actual presence of this one didn't do anything to change that view.

And then he smiled, and held out his hand, and before she could stop herself, her natural courtesy made her extend her own hand without thinking.

His fingers curled around hers, firm and strong, and she almost snatched her hand away from his. She just managed to resist rubbing her fingers on her skirt.

He knew, of course. She could see it by the way his eyes were amused now. His accent might be raw and rough to their southern ears, but she had no doubt that he was an educated man. His clothes were impeccable, and those finger nails were clean and buffed without being effeminate in any way. This was no Yorkshire tyke straight off the moors, *à la* Heathcliff...

"Is your father available, Miss Caldwell?" he continued in that cool, assured voice.

"I don't know...I'll see," Immy stammered, and fled to the back room, thankful there had been no regular customers in the shop at that moment to witness her lack of composure.

What on earth was wrong with her? It wasn't as though he attracted her in the very least. If anything, he reminded her too much of Morgan, with his dark good looks and his smooth and easy manner.

"Is there a fire?" her father said mildly, as she went storming through to him.

"Only in my heart," she said savagely, and then winced, knowing that such histrionics were more worthy of Daisy than her normally self-sufficient self! It seemed a long time since she had felt that way, however, she admitted, and from the way her heart kept leaping about in her chest for all kinds of reasons lately, it was a wonder she didn't suffer a heart attack.

Her father was even laughing gently now, and it was good to hear the sound, even if she had been the butt of his amusement.

"My goodness, something's definitely rattled you, hasn't it, my love? What's happened?"

Immy handed over the business card in silence, waiting for the explosion as he digested the gilt words printed on it. It was a vulgar card, she tried to tell herself derisively, knowing that it wasn't. It was perfectly tasteful.

"Ah," said her father without surprise. "Please ask Mr Preston to come through, Immy, and perhaps you would make us a pot of tea."

"Did you know he was coming?" she demanded, unable to grasp the fact that her father seemed so willing to sit down with the enemy and drink tea.

Or was she being totally naive? There was no point in being antagonistic, she supposed, when the young man in the shop was presumably a son or nephew, and not the almighty owner of Preston's Emporium.

"Darling, we might as well be sociable," Quentin said. "What's done is done, and there's no changing it."

"But what does he *want*?"

"I don't know until he tells me, and unless you're going to keep him waiting all afternoon, I suggest you do as I ask."

She went back to the shop, where Elsie was trying to keep up a stilted conversation with the stranger.

"Will you come through, please?" she said stiffly. "My father is expecting you — apparently."

"Thank you," he said civilly, making her ashamed of her churlishness, and resentful because she felt that way.

She shot a warning glance at Elsie as she followed Robert Preston into the back room and then disappeared to make a pot of tea and take it to him and her father. She poured out the two cups silently, offering milk and sugar, her hands shaking just a little as she felt the man's eyes watching her movements.

"What was *that* all about?" Elsie said at once, when Immy rejoined her. "Did you know he was coming?"

"Of course not! Father did, though. It's all so mean. Why didn't he tell us? I feel as if he doesn't trust us anymore."

"He trusts you to do the books, and that's trust enough, isn't it? You're so clever with figures, Immy; I wonder why you couldn't see that things weren't going so well?"

"Well, I didn't. Don't you trust me either?"

"Don't be a goose, of course I do."

"As for the books, it was little more than stock inventories mostly. The accountant did the real work."

"Or lack of it," Elsie pointed out.

"We'll probably never know the truth of it, and I'm not sure I want to know any more," Immy told her. "From now on, I'm going to take each day as it comes, and give up worrying."

If Elsie believed that, she would believe anything. But thankfully there was a small rush of bargain-hungry customers to keep them busy for the next hour, and when their father emerged with their visitor, he was smiling.

Robert Preston shook his hand and nodded to the girls.

"You'll join us for dinner next week at the Grand, then, Mr Caldwell? And if your daughters would care to be our guests too, I know my father would be delighted."

Immy held her breath as he left the shop without waiting for an answer. She couldn't help the feeling that in accepting this dinner invitation, her father had well and truly sold out. But worse was to come.

"Well, I'm not sitting down to dinner with them," she said indignantly, even though she had never been inside the Grand Hotel in her life before and had always wondered how it would feel to be entertained amid such splendour.

"You will, and you will be perfectly well behaved, Imogen," Quentin said. "You too, Elsie, though I think Daisy might be too much of a risk in polite company."

"But why should we go?" Immy said, even though they knew it was a command they couldn't ignore.

"Because I have just been offered the position of undermanager in the new shop, and I couldn't afford to refuse, since it will make all the difference to our futures."

"Well, I think that stinks!" Immy burst out. "How could you even consider it, Father? After being your own boss, and now to bend over backwards to the likes of those people—"

"I considered it, my dear, because if the worst comes to the worst, which seems most likely, and we have to put your mother in a residential home, I simply won't be able to pay for it unless I have a good job."

His face twisted as he spoke. The thought of sending his beloved Frances away was almost too much to bear, but he had known for a long time that it had to come. She needed professional people to look after her, and however much they loved her, the family simply couldn't give her all that she needed.

"Does this mean we won't be taking in lodgers, then?" Elsie said, since Immy seemed deprived of speech for once.

"Perhaps. I don't know. Obviously, I would prefer not," Quentin told her, deciding to be blunt.

"Just as long as you don't expect us to work for Preston's," Immy said. "Because I won't."

"That's a pity. Robert Preston said his father was particularly keen to offer us all jobs if we were interested. They're not unaware of how our circumstances will be changed, Immy. Give them credit for that."

"For trying to make us all dependent on them? For humiliating us even more! It's not enough that they've taken our shop away; now they want to gloat over us by having us work for them as if we're paupers!"

"*Immy*," Elsie said uneasily as her sister's voice rose.

"No, let her have her say, Elsie," her father said. "We're not paupers, Immy, and I hope we never will be. But I've done some very foolish things. It's my fault that we're in the state we are, which is why I'm doing my damnedest to put things right. I had hoped that my family would feel the same. Even Baz, for all his knockabout ways, has found himself some useful work instead of bemoaning his fate."

It was so rare for him to chastise her in this way, especially setting Baz up on a pedestal in comparison, that she almost wept.

"I can't imagine you doing anything foolish," she said, trying to prove her loyalty.

"Well, if you're fishing to find out what it is, you'll wait for hell to freeze, my dear," he replied, making her feel more rejected than before, because she hadn't meant that at all.

He strode off to the back room again, and she stared at Elsie miserably.

"I can't seem to please him, can I?"

Elsie gave a half-smile. "Join the rest of us, darling. You've always been his pet; it comes as a bit of a shock to find him so pithy, doesn't it?"

"I'm not his favourite, if that's what you mean!"

"Oh yes you are, and you always have been."

Immy felt embarrassed by her sister's frank words. She didn't set out to be a favourite – nobody did – and she certainly didn't want the rest of her family to be put out because of it.

"Elsie, I don't know what to say."

"Oh, for pity's sake, it doesn't matter! I wish I'd never said anything at all. It doesn't make any difference to the way we feel about you, anyway."

It wasn't the time or place to be getting emotional about family values and loyalties, but for the life of her Immy couldn't get the conversation out of her mind as she served customers with their bargain goods and rang up their payments. It was ironic, she thought, that they were so exceptionally busy now. If the goods had still been at their regular price, they would have been laughing.

"So are you prepared to go to this dinner at the Grand?" she asked her sister during a welcome lull.

"Of course. Daddy expects it, doesn't he? We have to show a united front, Immy. I thought you'd have seen that."

There it was again – that little bit of censure she wasn't used to. Or perhaps she was just being extra sensitive to nuances in a voice now, even if the words were artless enough.

"I'm going to see Helen again as soon as I can," she said, in an effort to sound normal. "Sometimes I think we've become too insular, Elsie. We're like Siamese quins."

"Don't you mean twins?"

"I was thinking of the five of us actually, though as you can hardly count Teddy, it should probably be quadruplets – no, *triplets*, since Baz is hardly there. And Daisy can be a bit offish at times—"

"There you are, then," Elsie said, laughing. "It's twins – just you and me, kid," she added out of the side of her mouth in the best Western movie style. "But I know what you mean."

"Do you?" Immy said, knowing it was Morgan who had led her to this way of thinking.

"Yes. We go out with each other, eat, sleep and care for each other. As well as being family, we work together, and we confide in one another, which is what best friends do. But that's not such a bad thing, is it?"

"No," said Immy, knowing there were plenty of things she didn't confide to anyone except Helen. "But there's a big world out there, and whether we like it or not, we're part of it. Preston's have proved that we're not the only ones who matter, and even our cosy little world can be shattered when we least expect it." She shivered. "I'm talking nonsense, aren't I?"

Elsie put her arm around her. "Of course you're not. You're thinking of all these war rumours too, aren't you?"

She hadn't been, but any reply was curtailed as the door of the shop suddenly opened and a couple entered to look around. The woman was young, the man with her probably her father, and he was wearing dark battle dress that looked brand new. On the shoulder was a strip of insignia proclaiming him as an air-raid warden.

The woman saw Immy staring at it and laughed, hugging the man's arm affectionately.

"I told him it was daft to be wearing it in the daytime, but it's just like my old dad to brag about it. They all love their uniforms, don't they, Miss Caldwell?"

Immy nodded, taking care not to look at Elsie's told-you-so face.

Chapter Five

The following week the girls dressed with care and shaking hands for the dinner at the Grand Hotel, still with the feeling that the invitation had been almost a royal command. After changing her mind half a dozen times Immy finally decided to wear her best pale green frock, which complemented her brown eyes and glorious red hair, and Elsie chose her favourite cream ensemble.

Daisy was openly envious that they were going to such a posh place and complained bitterly that she never went anywhere. Baz, on the other hand, couldn't have cared less.

"I suppose it's a sensible thing to do," Aunt Rose said dubiously. "Better the enemy you know, and all that."

"They're not our enemies," Quentin said evenly. "I'm told they're meeting all the shop owners in the row socially, and since I have decided to take them up on their offer of a job in their clothing department, the least I can do is be civil to them."

"*Et tu, Brute,*" Rose murmured beneath her breath, still *in situ* despite her earlier decision to go home a few days ago. Frances's slight cold had made her choose to stay and play nursemaid instead.

Quentin gave a heavy sigh. "Please keep out of it, Rose. I have to do what's best for my family. You're already getting your way over Teddy, and I'll hear no more about it."

Immy saw her aunt tighten her lips until they resembled a thin pink line and just managed to resist a giggle at the effort she was making. The brother and sister were old sparring partners, and she could just imagine Rose's joy on the day she met Bertie Painter and realised that he more than lived up to the sibling rivalry she and her brother had always revelled in. There was more than one way of showing love, and those two were certainly proof of that.

Finally they were ready to leave Vicarage Street. The girls sat tensely behind Quentin in the big old Rover that was to take them to the Grand Hotel.

Immy considered herself more worldly wise than her sister, if only because of her secret romance with Morgan Raine, and if her own mouth was dry, she couldn't imagine what Elsie's must be like. The hotel was grand in every way, and they were all awed by its magnificence as they entered the foyer at the appointed time.

Immy presumed that the man who came forward to greet them was the ogre, Owen Preston. Behind him were two younger men, one of whom was the fellow they had met the previous week.

"My dear sir," Owen Preston said, in the same flat tones as his son had used. He pumped Quentin's hand enthusiastically. "We meet at last – and not before time, after all the paperwork nonsense that's gone on between our two parties, as they call us these days. And these two bonnie lasses must be your daughters, of whom I've heard such good reports, though now that I see them, I realise none of it quite does them justice. You're a very fortunate man."

Such glib compliments were probably the hallmark of the canny businessman, thought Immy cynically, and shouldn't be taken seriously.

"This is Imogen, and this is Elsie; they're my two eldest," her father was saying, at which they murmured back politely.

"Aye, and a prettier pair a man couldn't wish to see. Now, you've already met my son, Robert. He'll not be staying in Bristol but seems to think I need a bit of watching over when I travel," he added with a bucolic laugh that probably meant Robert was quite correct. "T'other fine specimen is my nephew Joseph – Joe – who'll be taking over as manager of the new establishment. But you'll not want to talk about that now, and we don't need to stand on ceremony. This is a social occasion, and we'll have a drink to wet our whistles and get to know one another."

Once he was in full flow, they realised they hardly needed to talk at all and to their surprise they found themselves more relaxed in his larger-than-life company than any of them had expected. As the evening progressed the two older men developed an easy rapport between them, but that was more than could be said about the younger generation. Foolish or not, Immy still smarted at the thought that these people were taking away all her father's dreams and ambitions – even if he was able to so successfully abandon them, by the looks of things.

She couldn't stop thinking that Robert Preston thought himself superior to them, and at first Joe didn't say very much at all. He wasn't what she would call management material, Immy found herself thinking, but presumably he was more comfortable dealing with staff and customers than with social guests he didn't know.

It gradually dawned on her that Elsie was coming out of her shell more than usual, as if to compensate for Joe's lack of social skills. Two of a kind, maybe, she reflected. And it was herself, normally the more confident of the sisters, who found herself tongue-tied and annoyed because of it.

"Have I done something to offend you, Miss Caldwell?" she heard Robert Preston say at one point. It was surprisingly easy to have a few words of private conversation under cover of his father's frequent raucous laughter.

"No, of course not. I hardly know you," she replied.

"I'm sorry I'm not able to stay in Bristol more than a few more days, then, for I'd very much like to put that right. But we all have to be in York by the end of the week. My sister's getting wed."

"Oh," she said, not knowing what other comment to make. She didn't know whether to be more surprised that these giants of industry had a normal family life involving a sister's wedding, or by the fact that if she'd heard him correctly, he'd just implied that he'd like to know her better. Well, if he had, he had better forget it, because she would as soon snub him as look at him!

At that moment he smiled at her with that Heathcliff smile again and spoke softly.

"Don't hate us, Miss Caldwell."

"I don't," she muttered.

She wasn't attracted to him either – at least, only in the mildest way. And after Morgan, she had no intention of being attracted to any other young man for a long while yet. Maybe never, she thought dramatically.

She turned away from him as she heard her sister's laughter, and to her astonishment she saw her sister gazing up into the eyes of Joe Preston. To any astute onlooker, there was more than a tingling attraction going on there.

Immy felt shocked. Not because she'd thought that Elsie couldn't attract a young man, but because she had never shown a great deal of interest in them before. And to be interested in one of *these*, of all people…

"Well, well," she heard Robert say, and as she met his amused eyes she knew he had seen it too. "Worse than selling your soul to the devil in your opinion, I dare say."

She ignored him, seething. He clearly knew very well what her feelings were at that moment, and she wished they weren't sometimes so obvious to other people.

"It's what makes every young man fall for you," Helen had once observed. "It's the mixture of that smouldering look in your eyes and that cool, cool voice. Oh, and then there's that delicious laugh! I wish I had it!"

"You're mad," Immy had told her, her helpless laughter having prompted Helen's final remark. "And I do not have every young man falling for me!"

She remembered the silly conversation now, thinking that, of the two of them, it was Elsie who had Joe Preston looking admiringly at her and "hanging on to her every word", as the coy storytellers in the women's magazines had it. For a crazy moment she wanted to put her arms around Elsie and protect her and beg her not to be hurt. Like a mother hen, she thought…

"I'm afraid we must go," her father said regretfully, a while later, "but it's been a very enjoyable evening, Preston."

"We'll do it again when I come down next time," the other man responded, slapping Quentin on the back.

"And the name's Owen. There's no need to be formal now we've got to know each other. And no hard feelings, I hope."

"Not anymore," Quentin reassured him. "But I'm still curious as to why you decided to move some of your business down here in the current climate."

"All this war talk, you mean?" Preston said with a shrug. "Insurance is the word, Quentin lad. That'll take care of anything should it come to the worst."

"I don't know of any insurance company who'll pay out for an act of God or an act of war," Quentin said doubtfully.

"I do. It means I pay enormous premiums, but in return I've got a cast-iron clause included in the policy to pay out for war damage to any of my properties. It's called forward planning," Preston added, touching his finger to his nose. "Preston's were looking to expand, so why not come south, and why wait until the moon turns to cheese? I'm also a patriot, Quentin, and I prefer to keep my business in this country rather than selling my goods to those bastards on the Continent, begging your pardon, lasses."

Robert spoke with some irony. "Make no mistake, Mr Caldwell, my father will have us all in uniform the minute the prime minister makes an announcement."

"There's nowt wrong with that, lad. We saw enough of them conchie buggers in the last campaign. If I was still young enough, I'd be off like a shot the next time it happens, and so should any red-blooded Englishman."

"And Welsh and Scots and Irish, presumably," Immy murmured, realising that Preston senior had had more than enough to drink over dinner, and would benefit by sleeping it off as soon as he reached his hotel room.

"Oh aye, them too," he slurred. "Well then, Caldwell, if you must go" – he got to his feet, swaying gently – "we'll say goodnight to you all and hope to see you again soon."

"What a hoot, wishing us goodnight as if we were all the best of friends," Immy said, the minute they were back in the car again, and feeling unaccountably put out for no particular reason. "Hoping to see us again soon, indeed! Hoping to take over our shop, that's all, which he's already done anyway!"

"I thought he was nice," Elsie said. "He's not doing it to us personally, Immy. It's not a vindictive thing."

"It's calculating," she snorted. "All that stuff about insisting on a clause in an insurance policy to pay out if their property was damaged in an act of war. As if he's as rich as royalty or something! It's obscene. It's as good as wishing for bombs to fall – and who could possibly afford the insurance payments for such an eventuality?"

"Somebody who has become very wealthy by his own efforts, and isn't a fool with his money," her father said. "Now that I've met the man, I've got every respect for him. Your prejudice is far too obvious, Immy."

She didn't answer. She hadn't actually disliked Owen Preston, but she had felt uncomfortable at the whole command performance. Now she began to feel as if she was the only one who hadn't fully enjoyed this evening and found it a trial to sit through everyone else's mutual admiration.

"The young men were agreeable, too," her father went on. "Elsie certainly seemed to be enjoying Joe's conversation."

"I was." Elsie hesitated as if she would say more, and then changed her mind. But Imogen was feeling more belligerent than usual and wouldn't let her stop.

"Go on. What else were you going to say?"

"Nothing, really. Well, I was thinking about my working at home. Of course I know it's the right thing to do for now, and I expect to do my share of looking after Mother. But one day perhaps, when – well, one day – perhaps I could work in Preston's repairs department. Joe said he was sure there would be an opening for me if I wanted it."

Immy was crisp. "This 'one day' that you're talking about. Is that when something happens to Mother? Because even if we do send her away, there'll still be the guest house to run – *if* we ever start it – and I don't intend to be the sole skivvy!"

"Will the pair of you stop it?" Quentin suddenly thundered. "We've had a pleasant social evening, and I want to hear no more talk of your mother being sent away or my girls being skivvies. Now be quiet until we get home."

Immy bit her lip, appalled at the way she had let her tongue run on. The last thing she had meant to do was to upset her father when he had been in such a rare mellow mood. Nor Elsie, who was sitting hunched up in the back seat of the car now, as far away from her sister as possible. How quickly things could turn sour, Immy thought miserably, well aware that she was mostly to blame.

And all because she had suddenly become more unsure of herself than ever before. She had always been the confident one, the one the others looked up to, the oldest daughter, with a secret lover...Now it was all going wrong and she didn't know who she was anymore.

She must have made a small sound in her throat, because she felt Elsie's hand reach out for hers and give it a small squeeze. She could just make out her sister's pale face, lit by the glow of the street lamps and the headlights of the other vehicles, and she squeezed back, knowing they were friends again.

That was the best thing about families, she thought fervently. They always had each other. There was no such thing as having to make an elaborate apology. You just *knew*.

When they got home Quentin opened the letter he had been handed as they left the hotel. He studied it for a long time before he spoke.

"Well, I'm blessed. My instincts were right, then. He's not such an unfeeling fellow."

"What is it, Father?" Immy asked him, knowing the letter had come from Owen Preston.

"It's a formal letter to all employees of the row of shops shortly to be converted into a new Preston's store. Read it if you wish, since it concerns all of us."

Immy read it aloud for the benefit of Elsie and of Daisy, who had begged to be allowed to stay up long enough to hear about the dinner.

> "'*To all my loyal staff. By the time you read this you will have met me informally and we'll know something about each other. Some of you have already been offered posts in the new establishment. This to formally offer jobs to each of you. I shall need a considerable number of staff, and you all deserve the first offers. We shall not be opening*

until the middle of November because of the neces-
sary conversions, but hopefully it will be in good
time for the Christmas trade…'"

"An eye to business as ever," Immy muttered.

"Go on, Immy. Or is that all?" Elsie said.

She shook her head, reading to the end of the page.

"*'I realise that the interim time may be difficult*
for all who take up my offer of employment, so
I propose to pay each of you a modest retainer
wage from the day your usual business closes.
For your added information, the store will have
various departments, including general clothing,
books, toys, babies and children's apparel, and a
mechanical and tools section. If any of this interests
you, please respond in writing before your closure
date. I trust this will show my fairness to all.
Cordially, Owen Preston.'"

"Well! What do you think of that!" Elsie said. "And a modest retainer wage. I wonder what that means."

"It could be anything," Immy said.

"But a fair man, wouldn't you say, Immy?" her father insisted, and she couldn't argue with that.

Daisy spoke slowly. "It sounds different from what I expected. Working in the children's or toy department sounds like fun."

"Well, I won't be doing it," Immy said aggressively, resisting the urge to call them all turncoats. "We were always a small family business, and I don't want to be part of a big concern that will swallow us up."

"I suspect there may be plenty more of them in the future, darling, and you can't fight progress," Quentin said.

"No, but you don't have to like it."

–

Frances was well enough by the weekend for Quentin to insist tactfully that Rose and Bertie should go home and take Teddy with them. They had all had enough of each other's company by then, and they knew that if Teddy didn't go soon he would start rebelling at the idea. As it was, he couldn't wait to go to the Unwanted Dogs' Home and buy the pooch Bertie had promised him.

"We'll all be back for Immy's birthday tea, of course," Rose promised. "So you'll hardly notice we've gone before we're back with you again."

"Us – and George," Teddy said importantly.

"Who's George?" Immy said.

"It's what he's going to call his dog," Daisy sniggered. "Who ever heard of a dog called *George*?"

"It's his name," Teddy howled. "And I won't let you hold him, so there."

"Thank heavens for that." Daisy grinned. "Dogs are nasty, smelly things, like most animals."

"You won't want to meet our farming friends when you come to visit us, then, Daisy," Aunt Rose said smartly. "Their daughter's about your age and she has a couple of horses. I thought you once said you wanted to ride."

"I did once, and anyway, horses are different. They don't make doggy and piggy smells all over the place—"

"No, they just make horsy smells," Bertie teased her. "So I take it you'll be quite happy to meet Lucy, then?"

"I dare say," Daisy said with a shrug. "If I ever come down your way, that is."

"That girl needs a good shaking, Quentin," Rose told her brother after Daisy had sauntered outside. "She's becoming a proper little madam."

"Takes one to know one," Quentin said beneath his breath, with a sly wink at Immy, just near enough to overhear him.

She smiled back mischievously, thankful they were on good terms again. Her father seemed more cheerful than he had been in a long time. And if that was down to his – and Elsie's – decision to work for Preston's, then so be it. It was their choice.

As yet, she didn't know what she was going to do, except stay at home and look after Frances. Though not permanently, she amended quickly. The days of an elder daughter being obliged to be a companion to her mother were long gone.

Was it selfish to think that way? She didn't think so. Especially as Dr Wolfe had spoken very seriously to Quentin about getting Frances into a residential home quite soon. And after that...?

Immy couldn't think that far ahead. In any case, first they had to see Teddy and the relatives on their way, and it was more of a tearful goodbye than expected.

Teddy had been a little pain in the neck for a long time, but when the moment of parting came they all realised how much they were going to miss him. The girls cuddled and kissed him and smelled the lingering infant smell of him. He wasn't such a big shot yet, and right now, at just five, he looked young and vulnerable.

Even Quentin, who had never spent much time with his youngest son, looked uneasy, until Rose reminded him that hundreds of children as young as Teddy had been sent away from their London homes for their own safety, and would be living with strangers, so they should all look on the bright side.

Milking it for all he was worth, Teddy clung to them all and wailed for his mother, who seemed totally unaware of what was going on. Smilingly she told him to be a good boy and be sure to eat his crusts so his teeth wouldn't fall out.

Bertie finally broke up the uncomfortable goodbyes before they became too much to bear.

"Come on, old chap, or George will be wondering what's happened to us," he said firmly. "We don't want somebody else to take him home, do we?"

The house was very quiet after they had gone, and Immy couldn't settle to anything. Quentin had disappeared into his study; Daisy had flounced off somewhere; Elsie had offered to read to Frances; and Baz was out as usual.

Without warning, she pictured the Preston family still revelling in the joyous aftermath of a family wedding. She wondered if it would ever happen to any of them.

She had been so sure it would, and that she would be the one to marry first. It was the right order of things. But now she wasn't so sure. Now, with all the changes in their lives, and losing Morgan, she felt as cast adrift as an old ferry-boat without a rudder.

She grimaced at her own thought. What a state to be in, thinking herself stuck on the shelf at nineteen years old! It was far too gloomy around here today. There was only one place to go to cheer herself up.

—

Helen greeted her with open arms.

"Thank goodness. The parents have gone to Gloucester to see my grandmother and I'm bored, bored, bored!"

"I get the idea," Immy grinned. "And I need cheering up. Teddy's been banished to the country, and I have a horrible feeling I'm going to miss the little pest after all."

"Oh dear. So tell me what happened about MR," Helen said, with little interest in small boys. "Did you patch things up satisfactorily, or do I sense a hint of despair?"

"Sometimes I think you and Daisy would make a fine double act, Helen. You're both so dramatic!"

"That's dodging the issue, darling. Now then, what happened with the Welsh boyo? Tell me before I burst."

"It's finished," Immy said abruptly. "It *was* him I saw with another girl, and he didn't deny it. We argued, and I'm off men for good."

Helen was silent for a minute, and then she shrugged. "Of course you're not. There are plenty more fish in the sea, and you're not likely to be without a beau for long, Immy."

"Aren't I? When do I ever meet anybody? I don't go to charity functions like you do, where all the huntin', shootin' and fishin' set go—"

"You can always come with me, darling, you know that."

"Thanks, but I didn't really mean that. I'm stuck in the shop, and soon I'll be stuck at home. What am I going to *do* with my life, Helen?" She was as pathetic as any drama queen now, she thought, but she couldn't seem to help it.

"What do you want to do?"

"I don't know. Travel. Write books. Paint pictures. All the impossible things I'd be no good at!"

"How do you know if you don't try?"

"I think the furthest I'm likely to travel is down to Weston to see Aunt Rose and Uncle Bertie, or ride around Bristol as a bus conductress. How does that sound?"

"Bloody awful, if you're asking me seriously what I think," Helen said coolly.

"Thanks. I knew I could count on you to give me an honest answer," Immy said with a grin. Helen's plummy voice always made the occasional swear word sound unspeakably elegant.

"No, really, though," Helen went on, clearly seeing this as her crusade of the day. "What are you good at? Accountancy, in a small way. So apply for a job as an assistant to an accountant. You can type, so why not a secretary's job? Don't underestimate yourself, Immy. In my opinion, you're the sort who can do just about anything you put your mind to!"

"My father's going to work for Preston's," Immy said abruptly. "And Elsie's toying with the idea, though she won't commit herself fully yet. Don't you think it's a betrayal?"

"It's common sense. Is that the bee in your bonnet?"

"Perhaps. They took us out to dinner with them at the Grand the other night—"

"My God, Immy, and you're complaining!"

"And I swear that any of those Preston men could twist anyone around their little finger."

"Except you," Helen said shrewdly. "So how many of these super-gents were there?"

By the time Immy had explained about the garrulous Owen and the way Joe was so attentive towards Elsie, and got around to mentioning Robert, Helen's eyes were knowing.

"Aha! So do I take it the gorgeous Robert didn't come up to expectations on the flattery front?"

"I didn't say he was gorgeous."

"You didn't say he wasn't."

"Actually, Helen, since we've been talking I've had an idea." Immy changed the subject, ignoring the thought that she could be remotely attracted to Robert Preston. "Wild horses wouldn't make me work in that new store, and Mother will need someone around, so even if the others all turn traitor, I'll probably be the one to stay home…"

"Don't make yourself out to be a martyr, darling. It doesn't suit you," Helen said drily.

"I know," Immy said, more cheerfully. "But you're right. I can type and I'm quick and neat at it. So if Elsie can consider working at home, why not me? I could take out an advertisement offering my skills as a typist. What do you think?"

"I think you're brilliant, and I'm not going to make you more swollen-headed by telling you more than once. So what sort of things are you going to type for people?"

"Whatever they want. Letters, stories, wills," Immy said vaguely. "Lord, I don't know. I've only just started to think about it. I'll be a sort of jobbing typist."

"A roaming secretary," Helen suggested.

"Who stays put," Immy added, at which they both fell about laughing. "It's an idea, though, isn't it?"

"It's a wonderful idea. Where will you place your advert? In the local newspaper?"

"Ah. Perhaps. I haven't got that far yet. I may just put a card in a newsagent's window to start with."

Helen shook her head. "That won't do. You only get housewives looking for second-hand prams or women offering their services as dailies. You need to attract a different kind of people. And you'll need business cards."

Immy knew Helen didn't mean to be snobbish. She just lived in a different world, where people moved in a different way.

"My father could help. He has plenty of contacts. You could work for him if he didn't have old Miss Phipps, who'll be his adoring secretary until she's too old to crawl up the path to his chambers." But she said it without malice, and Immy shook her head at once.

"Thanks, Helen, but I'd be far too nervous to work in a solicitor's office. My skills are fairly limited – but if your father can offer me any small typing jobs that are beneath Miss Phipps's dignity, I wouldn't object."

"I'll ask him," Helen promised. "But at least you're looking more cheerful now, so let's decide what to do for the rest of the day and forget about boring work." Since she never had to do any, it wasn't difficult for Helen to do.

They linked arms as they left the spacious house and strolled across the Downs, where the grass was sweet with summer, and the graceful span of Brunel's suspension bridge joined the two sides of the dizzying Avon Gorge, with the winding ribbon of river far below.

It was a favourite place for the more fashionable folk of the town to go walking, to see and be seen. And if the elegant and honey-blonde Miss Helen Church attracted admiring attention, it was met in equal measure by her companion with the blazing red hair and doe-brown eyes.

"So now tell me more about Robert Preston," Helen demanded, never one to let go.

The past few weeks had been taken up with so much anxiety and nervous tension within the family that Quentin Caldwell had hardly had the time to read the newspapers properly. Usually, he scoured every inch of them, national as well as local.

He wasn't what some modernists called a political animal, but as a businessman he felt it his duty to know what was going on in the world. Folk liked to do more than pass the time of day when they came into his shop. It had always been something of a social occasion, time for a chat with an intelligent man and the opportunity to put the world to rights.

Now it was nearing the middle of September and closure day was looming, but just because it wasn't going to be his shop anymore, he saw no reason for things to be any different. Now that he had cause to think more positively about the future, at least on his family's account, he settled Frances in a deck-chair in the garden and took a rare hour to sit beside her indulging in his favourite pastime.

It wasn't happy reading, however. It never was these days, and it was no use burying their heads in the sand. War was coming – maybe not this year or the next, but it was inevitable, and only a fool could deny it. And only a madman or a fanatic would think he could overrun neighbouring countries and not have the rest of the world come to their defence.

"What did you say, my dear?" he heard Frances murmur as he swore silently.

"Nothing, darling. Go back to sleep."

"Is it night?" she said in bewilderment. "And where is my nightgown? Quentin, am I in bed with all my clothes on?"

As her voice rose in panic, he kissed her quickly, his eyes clouded with pain.

"You're in the garden, my love, and I'm here with you. Try to rest now."

He ached to see her concur as obediently as a child, when she had once been so vibrant and dynamic. It was all gone now, and she was dependent on him – on them all.

He remained as silent as he could as he scanned the article that had caught his attention. The government was urging the construction of Anderson shelters now, in advance of the air raids that could be expected in the event of an attack. They were pompous words, written by pompous reporters, uncaring of the fear they put in ordinary people's hearts. And the next reports were even worse.

Some factories were already being turned over to the production of thousands of gas masks which would protect the face and lungs. It was intimated that every person would soon be given one of these hellish masks and instructed how to use it.

For a moment Quentin imagined his beloved Frances being forced to put the rubbery, alien thing over her face, and knew she would simply choke. And Teddy too…and all of them. He wasn't a man given to panic, but right then he wished he had the means to remove every one of them to some far-off place where they would be out of harm's way.

But if you believed the direst pundits, there was going to be no such place left in the world.

He read on, all his former calm slipping away. He thought Frances was asleep until he heard her soft, care-free humming, as sweet as a nightingale, and his throat constricted.

Chapter Six

Owen Preston was nothing if not efficient. Another circular arrived to inform all ex-shop managers that, as a further gesture of goodwill to those who were joining his staff, he would install a telephone in every home, so they could keep in touch when necessary. And a week before Imogen's birthday on September twenty-third, the Caldwells were the proud possessors of their own black Bakelite instrument.

It was a grand gesture that impressed everyone, though to someone like Helen Church, who had never known what it was like not to have a telephone in the house, it was less of a wonder than it was to the family in Vicarage Street.

"You know what this means, don't you?" Quentin had said delightedly. "It means we can be in touch with other folk as well, including my sister for news of Teddy. Bertie can get an instant message to us through his Lodge."

"So his funny old Antelopes will have their uses at last," Imogen said with a grin at the thought of solemn and portly Uncle Bertie wearing the regulation Antelope horns for his meetings. "It's a good job their Lodge is in Weston and not somewhere out in the woods, isn't it?" She herself was thinking more along the lines of being able to telephone Helen whenever she liked, once she had got the hang of the new-fangled thing.

Quentin chuckled back as images of his community-minded brother-in-law flitted through his head.

"It gives us some status too, my love. We're not the cast-offs we might have been. It proves that Preston's take care of their people, and that's not something to be taken lightly. No, maybe their take-over wasn't such a bad thing after all."

His eldest son scowled, out of sorts because Enoch Bray's ferry-boat had been slightly damaged and was in for repairs. Now he had little to do but twiddle his thumbs all day. He hadn't even been taken on officially on a proper wage-paying basis yet, because Enoch was a stickler for getting the boy's parental approval before he agreed to it. And so far, Quentin hadn't given it.

"You've changed your tune, haven't you, Father?" Baz grumbled. "I thought Preston's was a dirty word around here. I thought we all hated their guts."

Quentin looked at him in annoyance. Big though he was for his age, his son was not beyond receiving a cuff about the ears if necessary, even though physical violence was not something Quentin entirely approved of.

"You just mind your tongue, young man, and remember who you're talking to. I'm not one of your riff-raff friends, and I won't have their gutter talk brought home here." It was hardly gutter talk – in reality it was little more than bravado – but Quentin didn't see why he should have his bubble burst by the likes of this squib.

Immy put in her pennyworth, supporting her father. "I don't know why you want to spend so much time there, anyway, coming home stinking with your boots caked in mud half the time, and looking as if you've been pulled through a hedge."

Baz rounded on her, his eyes gleaming with a kind of malicious triumph. "Oh yes? I suppose you'd rather spend your time rolling about in the long grass up on the hill then."

The small silence that followed seemed full of accusation and betrayal, and Immy felt her face go crimson.

"What's all this, Imogen?" Quentin said at once. "Do you know what the boy's talking about?"

"I can only think he's been spying on me and Helen," she invented furiously. "We often go up there where nobody can overhear us when we want to talk about private things, but now we know differently, don't we? We didn't know we'd been *followed* and *spied* on, and it's just the kind of thing this little sneak would do."

She babbled on, emphasising the words scornfully, and taking the initiative for all she was worth. Staring Baz out, her brown eyes bored into his, daring him to betray her completely.

At last she saw his gaze flicker, and he shrugged and spoke sullenly.

"It's all dull girl stuff anyway. It's not half as exciting as listening to the foreign sailors and the old seamen. They talk about faraway places and *men's* things. That's why I want to work with old Enoch on his ferry, and not have to listen to stupid girls all the time. There's enough of that at home. I wish somebody would realise it's what I really want to do and not scoff at me all the time."

He stared back at his sister penetratingly, so that she could read every little blackmailing thought going through his devious mind.

You persuade Father to let me work on the river, and I won't say anything about you lying in the long grass with a boy and letting him kiss you, was his message. What else might he have seen? Immy wondered in sick horror.

Well, she supposed that if he'd seen her the last time she met Morgan, at least he would know there was no likelihood of any of it happening again. Despite her resolve she couldn't help feeling a huge pang of loss for something that had been lovely and was gone forever. And with it, a deep fury that this little wretch had seen and overheard it all.

"You know, he's probably got a point, Daddy," she said, turning to him as if the thought had just occurred to her. "Apart from yourself, we're a household of females, and he hasn't even got Teddy to tease anymore, poor little love. You followed your ambition to open the shop, and I suppose it's only natural for Baz to have an ambition too. For what it's worth, he has my vote to do what he wants."

"I wasn't aware that I was asking for votes," Quentin said coldly.

"Oh, why can't we let him go and work on his old ferryboat and give us some peace?" Daisy said. "He never stops grumbling about the shop, and it gives me a headache."

Immy hid a smile at the dramatic declaration. Meanwhile, Elsie decided not to bother adding her voice to the debate at all, sure that Baz would get his way in the end. Boys always did, in her opinion.

After a few minutes, Quentin spoke reluctantly. "Well, you can give it a try – and we'll see how long it lasts when it comes to winter, when nobody wants to cross the river in the bad weather."

Baz gave a whoop of joy.

"You mean it? You'll have to give me written permission, mind, because Enoch won't accept me otherwise."

"Well, at least the man's got some integrity," was all Quentin would say, knowing when he was beaten.

As soon as she could get him alone, Imogen grabbed her brother by his shirt collar, and none too gently.

"Now you just listen to me, you little sneak. We're even now, and I don't want to hear another whisper about this business *anywhere*, in or out of this house. Do we understand one another?"

He didn't pretend to misunderstand, and nodded quickly, aware of how incensed she was. The waterfront louts had jeered at him that temper went with red hair. Well, he had that too, and prided himself on using his fists when they were needed. But his sister was older and just as fiery – and surprisingly strong, he thought, as her grip on him tightened.

"I wouldn't really have told anyone, not in normal circumstances," he defended himself, choking and spluttering.

She let him go, pushing him away from her in disgust, and knowing very well that he would have done, given half a chance.

"The little blighter," Helen said indignantly, when Immy reported the incident to her.

They were drinking tea in a cafe in the town. Immy had contacted Helen by telephone, but only to arrange the meeting – this was something that had to be relayed face to face, without any interested operator listening in. Immy was still getting used to using the instrument. As yet she had no idea how private any telephone conversation was, and she wasn't taking any chances.

"You did well to cover your tracks so quickly, though," Helen went on. "And your father believed you, of course. He'd never believe less of his angel."

"I'm anything but an angel," Immy exclaimed. As Helen's eyes widened, she went on hurriedly. "It's not what you're thinking, and I've told you so before. But that doesn't mean I didn't think about it sometimes."

"Crikey," Helen said. Her own senses had been completely untouched by romance so far. They were intended to stay that way until a certain knight on a white charger came along: she much preferred reading about King Arthur's exploits to the miseries of Jane Eyre.

"I've never heard you talk like that about MR before, Immy," she went on.

"Well, I'm not going to talk about him now, so forget I said anything. The last time I saw him was when he delivered Elsie's leaflets and asked for a larger fee than we expected. It was out of spite, I suspect, because he's not used to being turned down by a girl."

"That makes you pretty special, then, doesn't it?"

A smile replaced Immy's look of annoyance.

"I suppose it does," she said cheerfully. "Anyway, do you want to join my family for my birthday tea? We've decided to have a picnic on the Downs, since Dr Wolfe says he sees no reason why Mother can't be there. She loves the fresh air, and Aunt Rose and Uncle Bertie will be bringing Teddy for the day. James could come too, if he's around."

"Oh, you don't know, do you?" Helen said excitedly. "He's enlisted in the Royal Engineers."

"Already? But there's not a war on."

"Not yet, but you know what everybody's saying, especially now Mr Chamberlain's meeting that horrible little

Hitler in Munich for talks over Czechoslovakia. All the papers are full of it. Don't you ever read them?"

"Not if I can help it. Well, yes, of course I do sometimes," she amended, at Helen's raised eyebrows. "Father insists that we should keep abreast of national affairs, but I try to avoid all that stuff as much as possible."

"Immy, you shouldn't."

With a solicitor for a father, and a mother into Good Works, Helen could be just as intense when she chose, and clearly had decided to take a more serious interest in the state of the nation now that James was one of His Majesty's soldiers.

"I promise I'll try to catch up," Immy promised. "So will James be around for my birthday?"

"He might. I'll try to telephone him tonight. He's with his training regiment in Winchester, and Lord knows how soon they'll let him out."

"You make it sound like prison," Immy said with a laugh.

"It is, as far as I'm concerned. I bet he looks a whizz in his uniform, though." Helen giggled, her sombre mood gone. "He always played toy soldiers when he was little, marching around with a toy gun and making me be the enemy."

"Good Lord!" Immy said, laughing as the pictures filled her mind. "I suppose you fancy yourself in uniform as well – and you might have to wear one if it comes to conflict. We all might, like women did in the last war – or we may even end up having to dig fields to grow turnips. What a thought!"

They looked at one another as the idea began to sink in that this might not be play-acting at all, but very real.

"I'm simply not going to think about it, except to say that if it *does* happen, we must always stick together, Immy. We'll both be nurses, or both grow the damn vegetables, or drive cars for officers—"

Imogen hooted. "Oh yes! That's all right for you, but I can't drive a car."

"You'd better learn, then," Helen advised her. "But whatever happens, we'll stick together, right?"

"Through thick and thin," Immy said solemnly, and they shook hands over the table, before she burst into nervous giggles again. "Now stop it."

"All right," Helen agreed. "Tell me what I can buy you for your birthday instead."

Immy couldn't decide. There were only two things on her mind as she bicycled home again in the heat of the day. One was that she had begun to think it might be a very good idea if she learned to drive a car, and that she would do her best to persuade her father to teach her.

The other, gloomier thought was that Morgan wouldn't be giving her the small gift he'd promised. She shouldn't care…but it was hard to accept the blow to her pride caused by his discarding her so easily. Even if she had known she would never fully trust him again, he hadn't put up much of a fight to keep her as his girl.

He hadn't wanted her as much as she thought, and if she had any sense, she'd keep reminding herself that she didn't want him.

In the end, the birthday picnic was delayed for a week because Teddy caught a bad cold, and Rose wouldn't bring him to Bristol until he was better.

So the day of celebration coincided with the jubilant newspaper and wireless reports at the end of September that Mr Chamberlain had pulled off a massive success in Munich, and returned home to cheering crowds at Heston airport, with the news that there was to be no war. The Munich Pact had been signed, and an almost palpable sigh of relief seemed to envelop the whole country.

"Isn't it wonderful news?" Immy asked a handsome and newly uniformed James Church when her friends joined the family on the Downs in the middle of that sunny afternoon. "You needn't have bothered to enlist, James!"

"I wouldn't say that," he told her. "It's what I always intended to do, and besides, this is only the beginning."

"How can you be such a pessimist? I don't believe you, anyway. Don't you dare put a damper on my party, James!"

He laughed at her pouting face and stroked his finger down her cheek. "I wouldn't dream of upsetting the prettiest young lady in all Bristol!"

Immy's face went pink. He didn't pay compliments lightly, and as she caught sight of Helen's grinning face she remembered her teasing words, "You can always marry James." But she had never thought of him in that way before, and she didn't think of him that way now. He was an old friend, no more…

"Oh, pooh," she answered him lightly. "Stop teasing me and come and have some lemonade and sandwiches before Baz and Daisy scoff them all."

He laughed again and put his arm carelessly around her waist as they joined the others, the way old friends did.

"Now then, Imogen, what have you and this young man been plotting with your heads together?" her Aunt Rose asked.

"Well, James is plotting how to win a non-existent war, and I'm plotting how much of my delicious birthday cake I can decently eat without ending up looking like a barrel." Immy giggled, serenely confident that she had the neatest figure of all of them and never put on an ounce, no matter what she ate.

"I want some cake. Me, me!" Teddy bellowed, tidier than of old after Aunt Rose's fussing over him. The rampant George, the new Yorkshire terrier pup that he had adamantly refused to leave behind in Weston, got so excited at Teddy's shouting that he had to be restrained from trampling over the entire feast.

Quentin took charge, insisting that the pup be tied to a convenient tree before they all ended up having mashed cake and sandwiches for tea. But it was all so light-hearted on that blue and golden day, an afternoon of Indian summer, that nobody really got upset.

Immy felt a sudden crazy and irrational need to hold this whole scene in her memory and fix it there for evermore. She wished she had her box Brownie to do the job for her, but she hadn't remembered it. What a shame.

All her family and her closest friends together…her darling mother enjoying the sunshine…and not a war cloud anywhere in the sky. It deserved to be photographed for posterity as a permanent reminder of this glorious day.

There were other groups out on the Downs as well, and it was as if the newly buoyant mood of the country and the fair weather had combined to bring everyone out of doors. There were older couples, and a number of other families with young children and babies in prams.

Away to the right of them, too near to the edge of the steep cliffs overlooking the gorge in Aunt Rose's opinion, a child of about Teddy's age was having a small tantrum, and his nurse was vainly trying to quieten him and stop him screaming and upsetting other people. It was the only jarring note in an otherwise beautiful day, but few people took any real notice. The Caldwell party were all laughing and teasing Teddy that he'd never get George to do tricks until he was out of the puppy stage.

Teddy wouldn't give up, and by now George was yapping excitedly, rolling on to his back to be tickled. Everybody was taking turns obliging when Elsie suddenly spoke loudly.

"What's Mother doing? Where's she going? Daddy — oh, Daddy, stop her!"

They stopped tickling the dog, and everyone began crying out at once as they turned and saw Frances, her graceful arms outstretched, her feet skimming over the grass as nimbly as they had ever done in her dancing days.

They heard the joy in her voice as her arms reached out as if to embrace the screaming child, who had torn away from his nurse now and was staring at the vision in the floaty summer frock coming towards him.

"My baby. My sweet baby. Come to Mama, Teddy," Frances was crooning sweetly. "Mama will kiss and make it all better."

"Dear God in heaven," Quentin croaked as he rushed to cover the ground between him and his wife. Everyone else was at his heels, except for Rose, who held Teddy close, burying his head against her bosom as if to stave off the inevitable.

"Frances, come back," Quentin shouted hoarsely. "It's not Teddy. Teddy's here with us. Keep away from the edge, for God's sake."

As she heard his voice, she turned around in bewilderment, and the other child let out the breath he had been holding in a blood-curdling scream, as if he thought this madwoman was about to take him away.

The child's nurse began to shout at Frances, and it clearly unnerved her. They saw her teeter for a few seconds, her feet twisted and somehow tangled in one another, and then the terrified screams were hers as she plunged over the steep cliffs of the Avon Gorge and disappeared from view.

–

From then on one of the best days of Immy's life became the worst. The ambulance men told them that Frances had never had a chance, and by the time they had recovered her torn and bleeding body and taken it reverently away for examination and pronouncement, they had all realised that the next place for her would be the hospital chapel of rest.

Quentin was inconsolable. Crowds had gathered on the Downs, and there were many more on the river bank and the roadside far below. Some of them would be clearly thinking it was just another suicide, for which these cliffs and the suspension bridge were favourite venues.

The hell of it had been that the family hadn't been able to get to Frances quickly. There was no path down the cliffs, and the cars took an age to reach the valley far below. By then someone had already sent for an ambulance, and someone else had covered Frances's body with a blanket for decency's sake. All the family could do was cling together and weep, knowing the only consolation was that she must have died instantly.

Immy had wanted to scream at people not to cover her mother's lovely face with the blanket and to let her breathe…even though she knew how heartbreakingly foolish it was. Like their father, Elsie seemed numb with shock now, while Daisy stood shaking, her eyes terrified and distraught.

Rose and Bertie had swiftly cleared up all the picnic things and taken Teddy and George back to Vicarage Street before the child could see what had happened. They would explain the facts more gently later. Baz had gone with them, unable to face up to what had happened.

James Church kept his arms around Immy and his sister, as if to shield both of them. None of it helped. Nothing could change the fact that on this day of all days, fate had so cruelly taken Frances away from them, and in so ghastly and horrible a way.

"It's so dreadful for it to happen so publicly," Helen whispered, not knowing what else to say.

"It's dreadful for it to happen at all," Immy retorted through shivering lips. She gave a strange, strangled laugh. "But you know what I keep telling myself? I think that in a weird way Mother would have loved the drama of it all. She had an audience, and that's what she lived for."

"Oh Immy, that's an awful thing to say."

"No, it's not," Immy said, flinching at her friend's censure. "She'll have had her last moment of glory, because this will surely be splashed all over the local newspaper. Now everyone will remember her as she was, and probably ask my father to provide details of her earlier years in the theatre. And if they *don't* think about reminding everyone how talented she was, I shall damn well insist that they do!"

"Good for you, Imogen."

She recognised the voice immediately. A voice that was marginally less arrogant than usual, showing suitable respect for a tragedy.

She spun around, her heart thumping, knowing it would be Morgan, as curious as anyone else in the Gorge valley that day, whether they had actually witnessed the accident or simply heard the scream of the ambulance. They were all ghouls, thought Immy savagely, knowing it was human nature all the same.

Morgan wasn't alone. The girl she had seen before was there with him. They had obviously been out for an afternoon stroll, but now she had a notebook and pencil in her hand.

"I'm very sorry, Imogen," Morgan said roughly. "This is a terrible thing to happen, and we've only just discovered who the lady was. But if you want to let us know exactly what happened, I can promise you the true facts will get into the paper as soon as possible, instead of any garbled reports. Catherine's a trainee interviewer," he finished lamely, as Immy's eyes burned into him.

Since she seemed to have temporarily lost the power of speech, James assessed the situation and took charge at once.

"I think that would be a sensible thing to do, and far better than any wild suppositions. But as you can see, Miss Caldwell's in no state to give a statement. If you permit me, I can tell you exactly what happened."

"And you are?" the girl called Catherine asked, as James drew her and Morgan to one side, well away from eavesdroppers.

"A close friend of the family," he said.

There had to be an inquest, and the verdict was the expected one of Accidental Death, but long before that the local newspaper had given endless column inches to the once glamorous stage artiste, Frances Caldwell.

It resulted in the funeral becoming an even more harrowing occasion then expected, since it seemed that half of Bristol had turned out to witness it as if it was some kind of spectator event. "It only needs the sandwiches and deck-chairs," Rose said sourly.

Quentin was both moved and appalled at the crowds intruding on their personal grief, but Immy still had the macabre feeling that her mother would have loved it all, that she was somewhere Up There watching, and approving.

Because of the sudden interest in what most people living outside the area would have seen as merely passing news of a one-time star, the newspaper's coverage seemed to go on for several weeks. As other interviewers requested details about Frances's life and career, Imogen became the spokesperson, knowing that she was feeding that interest with an almost frantic desire not to lose her mother, and that in this small way, she was keeping her with them, still in their midst.

Since her father couldn't face it, she had been the one to search for her mother's memoirs and loan the news-paper the old programmes and posters that were repro-duced in full. Theatre managers and stage hands were interviewed, as well as prop designers and a retired dresser who had known Frances at the beginning of her career. All gave their version of the beautiful and talented dancer who had been out of the public eye for so long.

Eventually the family began to feel she hadn't belonged to them at all, but to the world.

"This has gone on long enough, and it has to stop," Quentin finally said harshly, when Immy asked if she could borrow his favourite photograph of her mother – the one that never left his bedside. "I want no more of it, Imogen. Your mother was the one who revelled in the publicity, not me, and now she's had her fill. Let her rest in peace, for God's sake, and stop tormenting me."

She stared at him dumbly, seeing the gaunt lines on his face that had never been there before. Too late she realised that all this attention was killing him. She ran to him and hugged him, feeling his silent sobs against her body.

"God knows I miss her, and I'll love her until the day I die, my darling," Quentin finally muttered, "but I had years of sharing her with the world, and now I just want to be selfish and keep my memories of her to myself."

"I understand, Daddy," Immy whispered. "It seems that you and I have been pulling in opposite directions, when we should be pulling together. I know now we have to accept what can't be changed, don't we?"

The others seemed better at doing that than she was, although she couldn't see into their minds and supposed that it might be their method of coping. Everyone had their own way of dealing with grief. She knew that. But she was the eldest, and her memories of her mother were sharper and longer. She couldn't really settle to anything. Like her father, without the shop to occupy herself, she seemed to be in a kind of limbo.

Condolence cards and letters kept coming, even from the Preston family, who had somehow got to hear of the tragedy. Immy didn't hate them anymore, but the cards served to remind them all of a part of their lives that was gone forever.

After the funeral Baz had immediately gone to work on the river, as if he couldn't bear to be inside the house any more than he had to. Elsie shut herself in her room for much of the time, and Daisy declared fervently that she no longer wanted to go on the stage.

In fact, she begged to be allowed to go back with Rose and Bertie, if they would have her, so that she could help to look after Teddy, at least for a while. And if she was too much of a bother she'd be quite willing to go and work in a village store, or something, she added vaguely.

"Are you sure about this, my love?" Rose asked her carefully, since it was such an odd request. "I think you should take your time over this. You always wanted to follow in your mother's footsteps, didn't you?"

"Not anymore. Nobody could," Daisy said simply. She took a deep breath, suddenly more self-controlled at sixteen than any of them realised. "I'm perfectly sure I don't want to do that anymore. Mother loved all the fuss, but I don't think she'd like the way it's been happening lately. I think if those interview people found out her favourite food and drink, they'd plaster that all over the newspapers too. It's invading her privacy, and ours, and I know Daddy hates it."

"Then of course you must come to us, my love," Rose said, hearing the note of desperation creeping into her niece's voice now. "It will be good for Teddy too, poor little lamb. He doesn't understand, and he keeps crying and asking for his mother. It's upsetting your father, though I don't know if we should be taking Teddy away just yet."

"I'm sure we should. I know Teddy can't help it, but he just reminds him all the time," Daisy said, wiser than her years. "Please let's go soon, Aunt Rose."

"The girl's right, my dear," Bertie said. "The sooner we all get back to some sort of normality, the better. And young Lucy will be more than pleased to show Daisy how to ride a horse, I'm sure. Daisy'll be competing in the local gymkhana before you know it."

"I doubt that!" Daisy said, with the glimmer of a smile. "But I do know one thing. It will be good to get George out of the house and back to the country. He's chewed up nearly everyone's slippers by now!"

—

The house was very quiet after the departure of Rose and Bertie, along with Teddy, Daisy and George. Imogen could hear the scratchy sound of the gramophone coming from Elsie's room, and when she knocked on her door and went inside, she found Elsie lying motionless on her bed, arms locked behind her head and staring at the ceiling.

"This was one of Mother's favourite tunes, do you remember?" she asked Immy without turning her head. "Sometimes I think I can still hear her humming it."

"Stop it, Elsie. It does no good."

"What? To remember Mother? Should we pretend she never existed, then? You're a fine one to talk, letting those awful newspaper interviewers have what they want all the time," Elsie said, brimming with anger. She sat up, hugging her knees to her chest. "I think you were enjoying the limelight, if you must know."

"That's a dreadful thing to say, and you know it's not true," Immy said, shocked.

"Do I?" She wilted. "Oh, I'm sorry. I don't know what I'm saying, and I'm just feeling lost and miserable."

"I know, Elsie. We all are. But you're not alone. We're still the Caldwell clan, aren't we?"

"Even if we're a bit depleted," Elsie said sadly.

Immy said nothing for a few minutes, and then said something that had been on her mind for a while.

"Shall I tell you what I think?"

"Go on. I know you will, anyway," Elsie said, turning off the gramophone as the music ended, to Immy's relief.

"I think you should forget your idea of working at home and take that job at Preston's new shop. I don't know whether Father will still want to take in paying guests now, and I daren't ask him yet. But you need to get out of the house and meet people, Elsie – and you haven't done anything with those leaflets yet, have you?"

"Hardly. It's been the last thing on my mind," Elsie muttered. "I haven't really thought about it."

"Think about it now. If Father's working for Preston's, it will boost his spirits to know you're there too."

"And what about you?"

"I'll probably stay home for a while and take in typing," Immy said, as if she had always known it would come to that.

"Well, that's a turnaround, isn't it?" Elsie exclaimed indignantly, not sure whether or not she liked the thought of her sister using her own idea. "And will you hire the dashing Morgan Raine to print your leaflets too?"

Immy shook her head decisively. "I definitely will not. That's the last thing I'll do. And don't even ask why, Elsie."

Chapter Seven

Personal tragedies always overshadow world events. It took a long while for the Caldwells to recover from the trauma of Frances's death, and even longer for the unwelcome ballyhoo surrounding it to die down. It was as if Bristol had suddenly remembered its once famous artiste and was doing its guilty best to keep the interest alive. But enough was enough.

As October slid into November Baz's fifteenth birthday came and went without fuss. Baz wasn't one for fuss, anyway. All he wanted was to notch up another year on his mental calendar and calculate when he could decently ask to leave home. Enoch Bray had said he could move into his cottage with him and his missis, if he was so minded, but as yet he hadn't dare mention it to his father.

There was plenty more to think about as the newspapers screamed out the news. The early euphoria over Neville Chamberlain's "peace in our time" declaration became a mockery as Hitler marched into Czechoslovakia.

Britain wasn't involved, but everyone said it was only a matter of time, egged on by the gloom-spreaders giving dire predictions of *when* the war would actually begin, rather than *if*. Some of the more daring newspaper cartoonists were already depicting various factions placing bets on the date.

...he old salts at the waterfront openly bragged about their part in the last one, firing Baz with enthusiasm to be in on something. He didn't know what, except that it had to be something to do with water.

Bristol was a traditional seafaring city. It was full of daredevil stories of the sea and of the old press-gangs who had forced men into service. There were hair-raising tales of those who escaped their clutches, disappearing into the many twisting tunnels under the old pubs such as the famed Landogger Trow, and accounts of heroes such as John Cabot and Isambard Kingdom Brunel and his great ships. Adventure on the high seas was in every true Bristolian's blood. Or so Baz told himself.

–

"Why would we have to get involved in a war, anyway?" Elsie asked one of her workmates in the spanking new Preston's Emporium, which had opened to a fanfare of publicity, or vulgar razzmatazz, according to some. "I'm not sure it's our business to interfere with what Hitler does."

"It is if he thinks he can gobble up the whole of Europe," the older woman from gents' neckties and cravats said.

"But we're not Europe. We're England!"

"Tell that to those who fought in the last one. Ask your father what he thinks! He was in it, I suppose." She gave Elsie an arched look. "Or was he a conchie?"

"He certainly was not!" Elsie said. "He fought in France like everyone else."

"And came back. Mine didn't."

"Oh Doris, I'm sorry," Elsie stammered, red-faced.

The woman shrugged. "'S'all right. I hardly knew him. I was only a kid when me mum got the telegram. But I still remember wondering what was going to happen to us, me mum with six kids an' all, and another on the way."

"And what did happen to you all?" Elsie said, humbled.

"Nothin' much. We had a lot of uncles who helped out."

"You were lucky to be part of a large family, then." She stopped, realising that Doris was laughing at her.

"Blimey, girl, you're a bit wet behind the ears, ain't you? I'd have thought, coming from a theatrical family, you'd have known what was what."

"A theatrical family?" The pain rushed in as she got Doris's meaning. "If you mean my mother, she was the only one involved with the theatre. The rest of us were just, well, normal. My father saw to that."

"He didn't mind, then – her mixing with all them flashy folk, I mean, and knowing what went on in some quarters."

"What exactly do you mean by that?" Elsie said, her heart starting to thump.

"Hey, kid, I don't mean nothing," Doris said, seeing how upset Elsie was becoming. "I'm sure your mother was whiter than white, and nobody ever heard a word against her as far as I know, but, by all accounts, some of them Hollywood film stars carry on a bit, don't they?"

"I dare say they do, but my mother was never like that." Elsie was stiff with anger now. "She always came home after a performance except when she was on tour, and then my father or my aunt went with her, so just you keep your nasty insinuations to yourself."

"Well, I'm sorry!" Doris snapped, ruffled. "Blimey, touchy ain't the word for it with some of you young 'uns."

She flounced off, but it put Elsie out of sorts for the rest of the day. She was scratchy with Doris and everybody else with whom she came in contact, with the result that Joe Preston, newly appointed manager of the store, asked her to come into his office at the end of the day.

She remained standing by the door of the office while he sat at his desk, pencil in hand, his good-looking face thoughtful as he looked at her rigidly held figure.

"You sent for me, sir," she said tightly, sure that she was about to get the sack.

"Come in and shut the door, Elsie, for goodness' sake. I'm not going to eat you."

She felt her mouth curve into the smallest of smiles at his words and edged nearer to his desk.

"So what's this fuss all about? I can't have my staff going around looking as if somebody's just died—"

The minute the light-hearted words had left his lips, Joe knew what he'd said. As Elsie's face crumpled, he came around the desk in horror, hesitating a moment before pulling her to him, and wrapping his arms around her. His voice was hoarse with embarrassment and concern.

"My God, lass, I didn't mean to be so bloody insensitive – and now I'm making it worse by blaspheming, aren't I? My tongue sometimes runs away with me. By now you'll have realised 'tis a Preston failing, but I was just trying to cheer you up, that's all."

"You've got a funny way of doing it, reminding me that my mother's just died," she choked.

Her voice was muffled, since her face was pressed so close to his chest, and, as always, she felt a huge sense of shock and disbelief at having to say the words at all.

Aware of their closeness, Joe released her gently, but he still held her hands, as if afraid she would take flight at any minute. He didn't want her to. With a fierce sense of shock he realised how deliciously warm and soft she had felt in his arms, and he wanted her back there.

He looked into her velvety brown eyes, shining with the tears she was too proud to shed, her cheeks flushed with pain and embarrassment and however many other emotions he and that wretched Doris had inadvertently stirred up in her.

Elsie felt his gaze on her. As she returned it, she felt an answering echo of something that she didn't understand, but which both frightened and moved her.

She almost leapt away from him, rubbing her hands down the side of her work overall in the smart Preston colours of blue and mauve stripes, suddenly as nervous as a kitten.

"Are you going to fire me?" she said in a small voice. "If so, I wish you'd tell me and get it over with."

"Good God, why on earth would I do that?"

He had returned to his side of the desk and told her abruptly to sit down. She did so quickly – if she hadn't, she was sure she might have fallen down. They all thought they were coping well enough after Frances's death, but sometimes it just hit you all over again...

"I haven't exactly been a model Preston's employee today, have I, sir?" she asked.

They all knew by now that it was the yardstick by which Preston's worked. Posters were pinned up in each of their stores to announce the model employee of the month. Most of the new Bristol employees had thought it pretentious and a bit of a laugh at first, until one of them got the accolade and preened for the whole month because of it. Elsie knew she was hardly going to qualify for that on today's performance!

Joe smiled gently, admiring the way she tilted her chin and stared him out, challenging him to agree with her.

"I have to admit that you have not," he said. "But since I also believe you were provoked into it, and having heard Doris's reckless words myself, we'll say no more about it."

She found herself sitting back in relief. She *liked* working here. Imogen had been right in saying she should get out of the house and see something of the real world – even if it was from behind a shop counter in the middle of town. And her old clients knew her and asked for her, bringing in their garments for her neat repairs, and the occasional order for a new hat.

"Shall we shake hands on it?" Joe Preston said.

As their hands touched, he blurted out, as gauche as any schoolboy: "I shall be going back to York for a week at Christmas for our usual family gathering, but the shop will only be closed for the two days' holiday, of course. When I come back, would you come to the cinema with me one evening?"

"Is it proper for a manager to ask a shop-girl out?" Elsie said, too flummoxed to say anything else.

"I don't see why not, but if you want me to ask your father's permission—"

"That won't be necessary. I *am* eighteen, and I'm sure he respects you, Mr Preston."

"Does that mean yes?"

She hesitated, flushed to her ears. "I believe it does."

"Marvellous. And Elsie, if you don't stop calling me 'sir' or 'Mr Preston', and start calling me Joe, at least socially, I shall withdraw the invitation at once."

She started to laugh at his teasing, because despite the greyness of the November afternoon, the day began to feel sunnier than any day had done for a very long time.

"Joe Preston has asked you out?" Immy said, when Elsie reported the news that evening. "What does Father say about it?"

"I haven't told him yet."

"And what will your workmates think about you hobnobbing with the boss? I'm not sure it's a good idea, Elsie."

"I wasn't asking what you *think*. I'm just telling you what I'm going to do. You're not my governess, Imogen, and I'm not a child anymore. Just because you've never had a young man interested in you doesn't mean that I'm going to stay a spinster all my life. The days when a younger sister had to wait for her elders to get married before she did are long gone, in case you hadn't noticed."

As she paused for breath, the temptation for Immy to inform her sister all about Morgan Raine came and went. It wasn't worth it. *He* wasn't worth it. Immy had seen him out with several other girls since the days of Catherine, so presumably that particular fancy had come and gone too.

"You're thinking of marrying Joe Preston, then?" she asked instead, sarcastically.

Elsie blushed. "Of course not. I'm only going to the pictures with him. And since it's not to be until after Christmas, because we'll be *far* too busy in the shop until then, I can take my time before telling Daddy. I thought you'd be happy for me."

"I am, darling. I just think you should be careful, that's all."

"I'm not going to do anything I shouldn't, if that's what you mean. I do know about things, Immy!"

"Of course I don't think that," Immy said, knowing her sister was as green as grass when it came to men, and having an enormous advantage over her in that respect

– if advantage it was. "I just think that if Joe Preston *was* thinking of marriage – eventually – that would be all right, I suppose. But if he wasn't, and if it all went wrong – well, it would be very difficult for you both, wouldn't it? Working in the same place, I mean. And for Father too."

"Oh, you're just being beastly, and spoiling everything!"

"I'm only thinking about you, sweetheart," Immy said in distress. She hesitated, and then spoke more softly, saying what was in her heart at that moment. "If Mother were here, Elsie, and still capable of understanding and caring for her girls, I know she'd be saying the very same thing to you."

Elsie bit her shaking lip, and slowly nodded.

"Perhaps I should go and ask Father's advice, then."

"That's a very good idea," Immy said, relieved that she wasn't to be the one to destroy her sister's dreams.

But to her surprise, Quentin didn't object, saying that Joe Preston was a decent, upright man, and that since everybody liked a bit of innocent romance, it wasn't such a bad thing for it to happen in these troubled times.

"It's only the pictures, Daddy," Elsie told him with a nervous giggle. "It's hardly a romance!"

But in her heart, she knew it could be. And when Joe left for York a few days before Christmas – and her father was elevated to temporary manager because of his experience in the haberdashery and clothing trade – Elsie realised how much she missed him.

It was then that she started dreaming about him and waking up with certain hot and shivery feelings she had never felt before. She began feeling not at all sure it was all going to be so innocent, either.

But first they had to bolster one another up for the first Christmas without Frances. Preston's was closed for the two days' holiday, and the frantic buying of gifts and wrapping paper was over. A decorated Christmas tree stood in the front foyer of the shop, but for the Caldwell family there was no heart for trimming the house or the usual festivities.

"You should get right away," Helen Church advised her friend Immy when she said how much she was dreading it all. Immy had described how the family had always played charades on Christmas night, and how her mother had loved it so much, laughing and clapping, even when she could no longer take part.

"Oh yes?" Immy said. "And where would we go? We don't have a seaside cottage in Devon like you. We're not—"

"If you dare to say you're not in the same class, I shall hit you, darling," Helen said fiercely. "In any case, we're not using the cottage at Christmas, so…"

"Thank you, but no thank you," Immy said. "It's very generous of you, but I know Father would never hear of it. It's only for two days, anyway."

Even they seemed to stretch endlessly ahead. The family were still lost after Frances's death, and, so far, they had done nothing about the guest-house idea. Privately, each of them thought it would never happen. In the meantime, Immy had advertised her secretarial skills and got a few responses, and done some typing for Helen's father, but that too seemed pathetically like grubbing for work. It wasn't her style. She knew she would have to get a real job, if only to hold her head up high.

The Christmas problem was decided, however, when Bertie telephoned to say Christmas was taking place at their house that year, and Rose wouldn't take any excuses. They were to drive down to Weston-super-Mare on Christmas Eve to be all together, which was how families should be. His and Rose's personal – and early – gift to each other had been the installation of a brand-new telephone, he added, which he was using now, instead of having to rely on the Antelope instrument.

"Your aunt's a good soul," Quentin said, when he put down the receiver, resisting a smile at the image the words conjured up. "And when she gets in one of her planning and organising moods, there's no arguing with her."

He was pleasantly surprised at having been made manager for the next week. It gave him back some much-needed status, although everybody said it had been on the cards all the time, and there was little resentment from anyone.

"Did Joe give you anything?" Immy whispered to Elsie when they were all bundling into the old Rover car, with Baz grumbling all the while at having to leave the city.

"Of course not!" Elsie said in astonishment, surprised that Immy could even ask such a thing. "We're not *courting*, Immy. Not yet, anyway, and maybe not at all. He's been far too busy to say anything much to me lately, and I sometimes think he may regret asking me out, or even have forgotten it."

If he had the hurt would be too great to bear, but she wasn't telling Immy that. She regretted ever having had any foolish romantic dreams about him at all, almost sure now that he had only asked her out on impulse and was far too grand to go along with it.

But she wasn't going to think about him at all for the next couple of days. They all had to be as bright as possible for their father's sake. Their parents' first meeting had been at Christmas time, and it had always been an extra special, magical time for them all. His two elder daughters were determined not to let him slip into despair.

Once Christmas was over, and there was a new year to think about, surely, they could start to think about living again. They just had to get over this hurdle…

–

Rose and Bertie lived in a rambling old Victorian house on a hill with a glorious view of the sweeping sandy bay of Weston-super-Mare. The house had originally been built for a large family with many servants, but since Rose and Bertie had none of either, they had filled it with assorted cats and dogs over the years. As Rose grew older, however, her increasingly finicky nose had begun to object to the various aromas the animals left behind.

Now, in the "beastie department", as Rose called it, there was only George, Teddy's exuberant pup. But Teddy filled a large gap in their lives, and there was also Daisy, though she spent most of her time whizzing down the hill on her bicycle to the Luckwell farm or helping out at the village store.

The first time Daisy had met the Luckwells, she had thought them a very odd crowd. With the superiority of living in the city, she thought the parents' caricatures of farming folk, large and jolly, with red-apple cheeks like the pictures in a child's story book. Ben, the son, was in his twenties, the spit of his father and already nearly as rotund.

Lucy was the real surprise. Daisy had fully expected them to have nothing in common at all, except that they were both girls, and she was impatient with Aunt Rose for even insisting she and Teddy went with her to the farm that first weekend.

"Do I have to go?" she had asked sullenly. "I know we won't like each other. She'll think I talk posh and she'll probably have hayseeds in her hair."

Rose snapped, "That's being snobbish, and I won't have it. Lucy's promised to show you how to ride, so behave yourself."

"I *can* ride," Daisy sulked.

"A *horse*, my love, not a bicycle," Uncle Bertie guffawed. "Anyway, when your aunt's made up her mind to something, you might as well get used to it and enjoy it."

Daisy decided she definitely wasn't going to enjoy it.

–

Lucy Luckwell, with a name that would have done justice to a music-hall star, to Daisy's thinking, was the opposite of her family in shape and style. She was thin and wiry, with long brown hair like a horse's mane, a ready smile and a pale complexion due to an illness that had apparently kept her confined to bed for the previous summer months. She was the same age as Daisy, which was supposed to make them instant soulmates, according to Aunt Rose. And to Daisy's agreeable surprise, she wasn't far short of the mark.

"Do you want to see Star?" she asked Daisy as soon as they arrived at the farm. Teddy had been taken off by Ben and the menfolk to feed the chickens and take a look at the pigs while the women drank tea and gossiped.

"Stars?" Daisy echoed.

Lucy burst out laughing. "Not *stars*, you goose. You can see them any night of the week. *Star*, my horse. Come on, I'll show you how to make friends with him."

She chattered on until they reached the stable, where there were several horses. Daisy eyed them apprehensively, her bravado deserting her at once. The horses were smaller than the dray horses who pulled the beer wagons about the city, but they were still much bigger up close than she expected.

"I'm not sure about this, Lucy," she said.

"Star won't hurt you. He's as soft as Weston mud. Stroke his nose, go on."

Daisy reached out a tentative hand to touch him, then drew it back as the horse whinnied gently.

"Don't worry, it's just because he doesn't know you yet," Lucy said confidently. "Blow gently up his nose."

Daisy staggered back as Lucy pulled her forward. "Are you potty or something? I'm not blowing up any horse's nose!"

"I don't mean like a force-nine gale! It's just to let him know you want to be friendly, and he's not going to do it back to you! Look, I'll show you."

She stroked Star's nose and then blew very gently into his nostril, as soft as a feather, and he nuzzled against her hand in response.

"You see?" Lucy said. "Now you."

Daisy moved gingerly forward, thankful none of her family could see this charade. Star responded to her by whinnying again and pressing his nose against her cheek.

"You see?" Lucy said in delight. "He likes you. Now you can do the same to Baby, and you can ride her if you like. She's a mare and a bit smaller."

By the end of the afternoon Daisy had formed two new unexpected friendships – one with Lucy, and the other with the piebald mare called Baby. She had also managed to climb on to Baby's back without sliding straight off again and by clutching grimly to her neck as well as the reins, she had stayed on for a gentle canter around the field.

"We'll have you entering the local gymkhana next year," Lucy said, confirming what Aunt Rose had surmised. "That is, if you're interested, and still around. You're only here on a kind of holiday, aren't you?"

Daisy looked at her dumbly. The afternoon had been so exhilarating, and she had been able to forget…

"I'm here because I couldn't bear to stay in Bristol after my mother was killed," she said brutally, wanting to wipe the smile off this nice girl's face, just as if it was all her fault. Nobody had the right to be smiling and happy when other people's hearts were breaking.

"I heard about that," Lucy said sympathetically. "It must have been awful. I know how I felt when my nan died last year. Nothing's ever quite the same again, is it? But everything has to die sometime. Animals and crops; it's all the same as far as nature's concerned."

She gave a brief swallow and carried on. "That's what my Gramps told me when I couldn't stop crying. He said my tears were probably doing a powerful lot of good in watering the flowers on Nan's grave, so to just keep on crying until I'd done enough, and she'd be satisfied."

"Crikey," was all Daisy could say after this tirade. "Don't you miss her, though?"

"'Course I do. I loved her lots, but I can't have her back, can I? Only in my heart – and now you'll think I'm a real loony. That's something Gramps said too, though."

"I think your Gramps sounds lovely," Daisy said, all her city toughness slipping away at this girl's simple logic. Country folk weren't all hayseeds after all.

"So do I. You can share him, if you like. If you want to be friends, that is."

"I do," Daisy said, as solemn as a vow. "And I'm probably going to be staying with my Aunt Rose for quite a while."

In the new year, Quentin Caldwell was officially appointed under-manager of Preston's Bristol Emporium, with a rise in salary and a sense of relief on his part that he wasn't going under after all. For a time his debts had assumed gigantic proportions in his mind, but now they were being paid off at a sensible rate, and he was beginning to see light at the end of the tunnel.

Frances's needs had been far more of a drain on his resources than he'd ever revealed to anyone, but he hadn't begrudged a penny of it, and if he could have had her back, he would have sold his soul to the devil. But he couldn't ever have her back; instead, they all had to make the best of their lives.

Now his daughter Elsie was officially courting Joe Preston, albeit in a discreet fashion to avoid shop gossip, and a nicer fellow he couldn't imagine for a future son-in-law. He gave a wry smile at the thought. If anyone had told him a few months ago that he'd welcome the prospect of having a Preston in the family, he'd have felt like punching him. But time and circumstances changed everything.

His smile faded. Time and circumstances were changing even more than the domestic doings of the Caldwells were. The government was sending out signals a mile high that war was coming. Before Christmas plans had been unveiled for a National Register of reserved occupations in time of war, and by February it had been announced that free air-raid shelters were going to be distributed to thousands of homes where the annual income was less than £250 per annum.

Quentin read the current newspaper report out loud to his daughters. "Priority will be given to London and other potential targets around the country. And Bristol will be one of them," he added grimly.

"Do you really think so, Daddy?" Elsie asked in alarm.

"I'm certain of it, my love. We'll probably have to build our own shelter to the specifications laid out. It has to be partly underground to be effective, so Baz will have to help dig out the plot for it in the back garden."

"He'll love that," Imogen grinned.

"I won't. I hate the thought of being underground in any way," Elsie said, shivering.

Immy changed the conversation at once, knowing she was thinking of their mother.

"Did you know Baz has been thinking about asking you if he can live with Enoch Bray and his wife, Father?"

She waited for the expected explosion, but it didn't come. Quentin's mood changes could be swift, and it troubled Immy more than she had let on to anyone but Helen. She couldn't decide if he was truly mellowing of late, or if he just didn't care what was happening to his family anymore.

Teddy and Daisy seemed very settled in Weston now, and it looked as if everyone was happy to keep it that way. Teddy was going to start at a nearby infant school at Easter, and if that didn't make him a permanent fixture in Aunt Rose's house, Immy didn't know what would.

"If the boy wants to live with the waterfront rats, so be it," Quentin said coolly in answer to Immy's query.

"Oh Daddy, that's not fair!" Elsie said. "Joe and I went across on the ferry last week, and old Enoch is as nice as pie. Doris says Mrs Bray's cottage is as neat as a new sixpence, and Enoch has to take off his boots and mind his manners before he even steps inside. I don't think Baz will come to any harm there."

"Well, that's all right then, isn't it? My family all seem to do exactly what they want, anyway, so I wonder anyone bothers to ask me anything at all."

He left them to themselves in the sitting-room, taking his newspaper with him and closing the door behind him with a bang that made them both flinch.

"He's lonely," Imogen stated. "Don't take his mood changes personally, Elsie."

"I don't. But I don't think he's lonely, Immy. He still has us, and his new position at the shop, and the customers and staff all like him. Why should he feel alone?"

The minute she'd said it she called herself a thoughtless idiot. Of course she knew why. The trouble was, when you were inwardly glowing with your own happiness, you didn't always stop to think how others might be faring.

"I'm sorry, Immy. I didn't think. It's because of Mother, of course. Do you think he'll ever get over her?"

"No. And in a perfectly selfish and shameful way, I don't want him to, either. Not if he ever thought of getting someone to take her place."

Elsie stared at her, surprised at the fierceness in her sister's voice, and shocked at having to confront a thought that had never occurred to her before.

"Get married again, you mean? Oh, Daddy would never do that, would he?"

"People do," Immy said roughly.

"Well, I wouldn't live here anymore if he did. I couldn't bear it."

"You wouldn't have to," Immy said. "You'd have Joe."

Chapter Eight

The vague plans to turn the house in Vicarage Street into a paying-guest establishment had been resolved by the beginning of the year. No longer content to stay at home and feel insular and isolated, Imogen had accepted the offer of a job as a receptionist within a housing agency and been given free advice about the guest-house idea.

The outcome was that Quentin had agreed to hire a builder to turn the top floor of the house into a self-contained flat with its own kitchen, bathroom and entrance. By the middle of March two middle-aged widows had taken up residence there.

While he was about it, the builder had offered to include the garden air-raid shelter at a job-lot price, which was both a comfort and an uneasy reminder of why it might be needed.

The outlay had been considerable, but the agent assured Quentin it was as good as an investment, and the widows now provided a reasonable income without making the Caldwells feel that their privacy was invaded. Cook had been persuaded to stay on – after throwing a fit at the thought of being head chef and bottle-washer for a crowd of strangers, as she called it – and a daily help was hired to "do for" the tenants.

Imogen liked the new arrangement. Like her father, she and Elsie were out all day, and it made her feel that they were now a proper business family.

It wasn't the family business of old, but she felt they had gradually made a successful move from despair into something positive.

But if things seemed more buoyant on the home front in the early months of 1939, they were less so generally. It hadn't helped the general anxiety when a group of volunteer ARP personnel had invited people to come to the hall near Vicarage Street and bring along their gas masks for a demonstration on the fitting and wearing of those items for varying periods of time. This move, intended to gee up any lethargy on the public's behalf, made the advent of war seem all too real – although most people were beginning to see it coming.

Many people turned up at the hall out of curiosity, to laugh and joke with their neighbours at the alien beings they represented in the hideous masks. And more than one section of the public declared they would never wear the beastly things; they would rather die from the inhalation of mustard gas, or whatever else the Germans sprayed them with.

"Some of them haven't got a clue!" Quentin Caldwell snapped. "The young 'uns weren't around for the last lot, and the old 'uns seem to have forgotten what it was like. Perhaps they think it's better to live in ignorance than to remember."

"It's better than not living at all," Immy murmured, knowing why her father was extra tetchy.

The anniversary of her parents' wedding was in March, and it would be a good thing when the day had come and gone. Each anniversary that came along had its significance, and there was some truth in the saying that it took a year before the mind could accept what it knew to be true.

There was always the nostalgia and pain of looking back to what was happening this time last year...or the year before that... or any of the years that made up the tapestry of their lives together.

The end of March was also the time of one of the local gymkhanas in and around Weston. The Caldwells planned to spend the weekend at Rose and Bertie's for the event, since both Lucy Luckwell and Daisy were taking part. Daisy had taken to riding a horse the way she took to everything else, with great enthusiasm and determination to be the best.

The only one of the family who refused to go was Baz, now firmly settled in the Brays' cottage and totally bored by anything that had four legs.

"I'm surprised you and Elsie could be spared from your shop duties, Quentin," Rose said, after she had greeted them, George had run rings around them, yapping excitedly at their heels and trying to lick everyone at once, and they had all exclaimed at how big Teddy was getting now.

"That's what comes of being under-manager," her brother said smugly. "There are certain advantages to be had, and a Saturday off occasionally is one of them."

"It doesn't hurt that the manager's besotted with the undermanager's daughter either, I dare say," Rose murmured.

"I wouldn't say he's besotted with me," Elsie said with a nervous giggle, knowing very well that he was, because he had told her so. Not in those exact words, of course; his had been far more romantic.

Joe was definitely a romantic, she thought, her heart swelling with love. In her moonstruck state she wished her elder sister could find a young man too.

Apart from the housing estate agent, who was forty if he was a day, she never even mentioned anyone. Oh, except James Church now and then – but he was serving somewhere with his regiment, and Immy hadn't seen him in months.

But she mustn't think of Joe to the exclusion of all else, Elsie reminded herself. This was to be Daisy's big day. They had left Bristol early to be in Weston before midday, so that they would all be able to cheer her and Lucy on at the gymkhana that was being held at the Luckwells' farm.

Before arriving at Rose and Bertie's house on the hill, they had driven along the seafront to get a welcome breath of sea air and watch the diminishing tide go out, leaving the town sand-locked – and "mud-locked", as Rose called it. Bertie always added importantly and predictably that it happened because the Bristol Channel had one of the highest rise and falls of tide in the world, so at least the sand got well laundered every day. And the heaps of seaweed that were washed up really *didn't* smell too bad…

Daisy came into the house with the speed of a whirlwind, having been let off her afternoon stint at the village store for this special occasion. She hugged and kissed everyone, and the excitement on her face made her extraordinarily beautiful. She was so much like Frances that Imogen drew in her breath and hoped it wouldn't upset her father to see it.

Immy was also struck by how much her sister had filled out and altered in the few months she had been here. The sea and country air was patently doing both her and Teddy a power of good.

"Lucy expects to win some rosettes, and I suppose I just *might* get one," Daisy told them with a laugh. "But you just wait until you see me on Baby. Even Ben Luckwell says I'm a natural. He doesn't normally bother with girls, but he comes to watch us jump the practice hurdles sometimes."

"He's got two sisters to be proud of now, that's why," Bertie told her.

Daisy laughed again. "I doubt he thinks about it like that! You know Ben; if he's proud of anything it's fattening up his old pigs and getting the best price for them at Yatton market."

Immy listened to her in amazement. It was so unlike the starry-eyed Daisy of old, who had always wanted to follow in her mother's dancing footsteps. Here she was, sounding more like a farmer's daughter herself.

Quentin clearly saw it too. "You're happy down here in the sticks then, are you, my love? Not yearning to come home again and keep your old dad company in his old age, now that everyone's deserted me?"

"You're not old!" Daisy protested. But as if some sixth sense made her realise what was behind the question, she danced across the room and hugged him. "And you'll always be my Daddy, no matter what."

"This isn't the sticks, either," Rose told him smartly. "And Daisy's free to go home whenever she wants to. She knows that. We're only borrowing her, Quentin."

It was quiet for a moment; then, before the atmosphere became more tense and emotional than any of them wanted, Bertie spoke again.

"We're getting another one soon. Maybe even two," he said. "You know what your sister's like, Quentin. Always a glutton for punishment, as they say."

"Another what?"

"Child. Evacuee. Applied to the Town Council, she did, and said we've got plenty of room, so if they want to send us another one – or two – they could," he said, hardly able to disguise his pride. "We haven't heard anything yet, though."

"Good Lord, Aunt Rose, aren't you brave!" Immy exclaimed. She turned to her brother. "Auntie might get another one like you, Teddy," she teased him.

"I hope we do. It'll be company for him, and Bertie can take them both fishing and keep them out of my hair when I'm trying to do my baking." But Rose was smiling as she said it.

Because there were so many of them they drove in two cars to the Luckwell farm. It was a fine spring day, with no sign of the British rain that could make such an event a wash-out.

Daisy left them to explore the stalls selling home-made preserves and cakes made by the ladies of the WI, cartons of young plants, saplings wrapped in balls of soil, and more bric-a-brac than ever found its way to the local scrapyard.

The next time any of them saw her, she was with Lucy, both of them elegant in jodhpurs, white shirts and riding hats. The Caldwells hardly recognised the young lady their youngest girl had become.

"Did you buy her all this kit?" Quentin asked his sister.

Rose shrugged. "You have to indulge me if I spoil them sometimes, Quentin. What else do I have to spend my money on if not my brother's children?"

It was one of the rare times she alluded to the sadness of not having any of her own, and she turned away, not inviting further comment.

The centre of the field had been roped off and set up with hurdles and jumps, and during the warm afternoon the competitors took their turns in the various events to the accompaniment of loudspeaker announcements and generous applause for the winners of each trial.

Teddy quickly became bored with it all, and when Ben Luckwell offered to take him – and any other children who wanted – to see the animals being fed, nobody complained.

By the time he left the field, now grandly called the arena, there was a trail of small bodies following him.

"He's a love with the young 'uns," Mrs Luckwell said comfortably, beaming at them. "He might be fourpence short of a bob, and he allus has been in his big old clumsy way, but he'd make somebody a lovely wife," she added. She shrieked with laughter at her own joke, as she went around smiling and welcoming everyone visiting the farm that day.

"If you dare say there's a catch for me, I shall thump you," Immy murmured beneath her breath to Elsie as they watched his lumbering frame disappear.

"I wouldn't dare," Elsie grinned back. "Not when you've got the delectable James Church hovering in the background. Oh, and I forgot to tell you the worst news. Robert Preston's coming down here for all of May, and Joe has to go back to the York store. Joe says his uncle's always been keen for his managers to do that kind of exchange, and even though they're family, they have to do it too. He says it keeps them on their toes – but I don't see why Joe has to go away so soon. I shall miss him like fury."

She went on prattling and grumbling, but Immy hardly listened to the rest of it. She was remembering the dinner at the Grand Hotel, and Robert Preston saying he wished he was staying in Bristol because he'd like to get to know her better. She recalled her instinctive reaction – that she was glad he was going away, because he was too dangerously attractive.

She hadn't put the feeling into words or even coherent thought at the time, but the idea was indubitably in her head now – together with the quickening of her heartbeat, and the image of his face, which was suddenly so vivid in her mind that he might have been standing in front of her.

"Immy, are you all right? I swear you haven't been listening to a word I've been saying!"

She blinked as her sister's face came into view.

"Of course I'm all right," she said crossly. "I just hear so much about Joe's virtues that my mind sometimes drifts."

"Well, I'm sorry!"

She was contrite at once. "Oh Lord, I didn't mean to be rude. I know he's a lovely man, and I'm truly happy for you, Elsie. I wasn't really concentrating because I wanted to be sure we didn't miss Daisy's event," she invented wildly.

She was angry with herself for allowing her heart to give even a single lurch at the thought of seeing Robert Preston again. After the disastrous affair with Morgan, she had vowed to beware of smooth talkers, especially rugged young men with a brooding Heathcliff appearance, who looked as if they'd be more at home tramping the moors than managing a shop.

Now she was doing it again, she thought in annoyance. She was letting him into her thoughts and her mind, when she had every intention of keeping him out.

"Here they are, then," Elsie was saying, as the tinny voice on the loudspeaker announced the hurdle race for the sixteen to eighteen-year-olds.

Immy forced herself to concentrate. It was what they were here for, to encourage Daisy in the faint hope of her getting a rosette, and to cheer Lucy on in the certainty that she would.

"Thank goodness we left George at home," Rose remarked, seeing that several noisy dogs had to be restrained by their owners every time an announcement was made. "Just imagine what he'd be like."

"I'd rather not," Immy said. "I don't want to imagine what he's doing to your house either, Aunt Rose."

"Oh, I think he's got over the wild puppy stage of tearing everything to bits now."

"You hope," Elsie added as an aside.

But there was no more time to speculate on what George might or might not be doing. The riders were coming into the arena.

"She looks so grown up," Quentin said, as if he had only just noticed the air of confidence with which his youngest daughter sat astride Baby.

"So she should. She's nearly seventeen," Rose said.

"She's still a child—"

"She's the same age Frances was when you met her," Rose pointed out, as if determined to keep her sister-in-law's name alive, since he seemed just as determined not to mention her at all. "And only a year younger than her mother was when you married her, Quentin."

"That was wartime," he said abruptly. "And a very long time ago."

"If you two don't stop talking and glaring at one another, we shall miss the start," Imogen said, admonishing her elders. Sometimes they needed it – those two could bicker as volubly as siblings of any age.

The starter's pistol went off, and the race began. The spirit of the afternoon was light-hearted, and the competitors raced around the arena to the accompaniment of cheers and screams from their supporters.

As expected, Lucy was easily the best rider in her category and she finished with a flourish, knowing she would take the blue rosette.

Daisy came a creditable fourth. It meant she took nothing, but she was triumphant at having finished the course at all and proved to her family that she could do something other than serve in a shop or make hats or type at a fair rate of knots. When you had two clever older sisters, you had to prove yourself at something.

At that moment one of the excitable dogs who had caused problems for his owner suddenly broke free of his lead and went tearing towards the horses in the small winners' enclosure, circling their legs and barking madly.

Thinking he was going to injure Star, Lucy shouted at the dog and automatically kicked out at him, forgetting that her feet were still in the stirrups. As she leaned over Star's flank, he seemed to stumble, and she lost her balance and cried out as she fell sideways to the ground. Her foot was still caught, and Star stamped the ground nervously, dragging her forward as she screamed at him to stay still.

It all happened so quickly that only those near to her were really aware of what was happening, and the main crowd of spectators saw little of the incident.

Daisy had a clear view, however, and immediately saw the potential danger. If Star really got spooked by the dog, who was still barking frantically and being pulled away by his red-faced owner, Daisy knew the horse could drag

Lucy along the ground or even trample her. She wasn't about to let that happen.

In the general confusion, she ran forward and pulled at Star's reins, talking soothingly to him and gentling him for all she was worth. His eyes were rolling, and she caught hold of his nose, stroking him and breathing softly into him, while Lucy tried to extricate herself from the stirrup and struggled to get away from those agitated hooves.

"I'll take the nag, girl," she heard Ben Luckwell say, appearing as if from nowhere. "You'd best let somebody see to our Lucy now."

Daisy blinked, realising that the small group of people nearby were applauding her and praising her skill with the horse. She was less concerned with that than with taking in what Ben had said, however. Lucy wasn't really hurt, was she?

Her friend was still sitting on the ground, holding her ankle and groaning, and Daisy sank down beside her as the call went out for the St John ambulance people to come to the winners' enclosure at once. One look at the ankle and Daisy knew it was sprained. It was swelling inside Lucy's boot, and Daisy knew it would already be turning a lovely mixture of purple and red.

"I feel sick," Lucy said.

"Take deep breaths and don't close your eyes," Daisy instructed at once. "Keep looking ahead."

"God, it hurts," Lucy muttered. "I have to get my boot off," she added, tugging at the laces.

"No, don't do that. You've got to keep it on until you get it seen to properly."

"You seem to know a blooming lot about it," Lucy said, the stinging pain making her aggressive.

"It happened to my mother during a performance. I was watching in the wings, and I can only have been about eight years old, but I can still remember the doctor's instructions."

"The young lady's quite right – but you can leave it to us now, my dear," said a male voice.

The St John ambulance men had arrived at last with their bag of tricks and were kneeling down beside them both. By now Lucy's mother had reassured herself that it was only a slight accident and was busily announcing to everyone that her daughter was perfectly all right, and that the next event would continue after a short interval.

Whatever else happened, the show must go on. Daisy knew that. Her mother would have approved. As other hands tended to Lucy and a stretcher carried her into the farmhouse, she followed on behind, feeling suddenly nauseous herself.

"You'd better sit down, love," she heard the second ambulance man say. "It takes folk that way after the event sometimes. But you did well to keep your head. Got the makings of a proper little nurse, I'd say."

He turned away from her as her colour began to come back and concentrated on Lucy. "Now then, let's see to this poor ankle and get it strapped up before the doctor comes to take a look. There'll be no more riding for you for a while, my duck."

"Never mind; I'll come and cheer her up," Daisy forced herself to say. Lucy gave a squeal of pain as they examined the ankle. "I think I'm off riding for a bit, anyway."

It had only ever been a pleasant pastime, and now she had other things to think about. She had always had a butterfly mind, but not in the way her family used to tease her about. She had flitted from one airy-fairy idea to the next because she hadn't ever been able to make up her mind what she really wanted to do. But now she knew. She was going to be a nurse.

–

"It's just another fad," Imogen said in the car on the way back to Bristol on Sunday afternoon. "We all know what Daisy's like. This week she wants to be a nurse. Next week it'll be something else."

"I'm not so sure it will," Elsie said. "She seemed pretty determined about it."

"She always does, but Aunt Rose will sort her out. She's going to take her along to her volunteer first aid class, and she's also got an old medical book for Daisy to read. Once she discovers all the nasty things a nurse has to do and the thousand and one ailments there are, I bet she'll start feeling squeamish and change her mind."

They were both laughing by the time she had finished speaking, but to Immy's surprise her father was not.

"I think you do the girl an injustice. Nursing's an honourable profession, and if Daisy does decide it's what she wants to do, I shall back her one hundred per cent. And I'll tell you something else. Your mother would be proud of her."

"Oh, Daddy, I know she would!" Immy agreed hurriedly, moved by his words. He rarely spoke of Frances these days. She was a taboo subject, since his memories of her were so bittersweet.

It was odd to think Daisy's new ambition might be the catalyst that would make him think differently. That, and Aunt Rose's mission to never let Frances be forgotten. Not that she *was*, or ever could be. But they should all take

143

heart and speak of her as naturally as possible in future, the way Rose did.

"I was amazed that Daisy remembered the doctor's instructions when Mother had her bad sprain, though. Daisy was such a little thing at the time – do you remember, Father?" Immy went on bravely.

"Of course I remember," Quentin said after a moment's pause. "For a while we wondered if Frances would ever dance again – but *she* knew she would, no matter what the doctors said." The pride in his voice was almost tangible. "Nobody was going to take that away from her."

"Nobody can take her away from us, either," Elsie said softly, unerringly following Imogen's lead. "Not as long as we can still remember."

"I know, my dears. But now, if you two don't let me concentrate on my driving I shall probably have us all in the ditch!" Quentin went on crisply. The girls both knew he had turned a small corner, however, and that they had helped him do it. In the back seat of the car, they reached out and squeezed each other's hands for a moment, each blessing Daisy for being such an unlikely angel.

"Imogen," Quentin said a little while later, "if you still want me to give you a few driving lessons, you'd better take advantage of my generous mood. We'll start after the shop closes tomorrow evening, God help me!"

"Wonderful!" Immy said in delight. The idea had been abandoned for so long she had all but forgotten it and was sure he'd had no heart for it.

By the time they returned home to Vicarage Street it was still a mellow early evening, and after a wash and change of clothes, she bicycled up to Helen's house to report the weekend's happenings.

"You're joking," Helen stated in amazement, when she heard the news about Daisy. "She'll freeze the minute she sees a blob of blood on somebody's finger."

"Actually, I don't think she will." Immy came quickly to her sister's defence. "I think perhaps the idea has always been there, deep down. I've been thinking back to all sorts of occasions when she played the little nurse, even persuading Elsie to make her a nurse's outfit one Christmas so she could look after Teddy when he was born."

"Playing at being a nurse is a bit different from the real thing, darling," Helen said mildly. "But good luck to her if that's what she wants to do. She'll probably be in her element when we go to war, anyway. Imagine having all those vulnerable wounded soldiers depending on you." She gave an elaborate sigh, her eyes mischievous. "It's quite a thought, isn't it, Immy? I might even consider becoming a nurse myself."

"I thought you weren't interested in men."

"I never said I wasn't interested. I just haven't found the right one yet. But watch out for fireworks when I do!"

Immy was thoughtful. "Do you think you'll ever fall in love, hook, line and sinker, then? Enough to throw off all your inhibitions, I mean, and – well, *do* things?"

"Lord knows. Probably, if he's masterful enough." Helen laughed easily, since she had never been tested. "Why, would you? *Have* you? You said you hadn't done anything with MR—"

"I didn't say I hadn't done *anything*. Just not *it*. Of course not *it*!"

"What, then?" Helen said. "You've got to tell me now, Immy. As your best friend, I demand it."

"I don't even want to remember him. But if you *must* know, he touched me here. Pressed me tight, I mean."

She passed her hand over her breast, feeling an idiot as she did so. Fast girls might be complacent about such things, but she wasn't fast and never had been. Despite having a glamorous mother who some might think of as bohemian, Frances had always taught her daughters to be virtuous and modest, the way good girls should be.

Just sometimes, however, Immy had wondered what it might be like to be less inhibited. Morgan Raine had certainly proved that she had a sensuous nature lurking beneath her air of Caldwell respectability.

She wished Helen hadn't stirred it all up again. She didn't want him anymore, nor think of him anymore, but she couldn't deny the passionate feelings he had awoken in her.

"What was it like, then? Him pressing your bosom, I mean?" Helen persisted. "I only ask in the name of research, Immy."

"Well, it's not much different from when you wash yourself in the bath. You have to touch them then, don't you?" Immy said crossly, knowing it was totally, erotically different to have a man's hand caressing them. But there were some things you just couldn't share, even with your best friend.

"I refuse to talk about MR anymore," she said. "The other thing I came to tell you was that Father's decided to teach me to drive at last."

"Hooray. So if we do have to join up we'll be able to put our names down as drivers for the officers. You meet a much better class of person that way," she added, only half serious.

Immy burst out laughing. "Oh Helen, you really are the most terrible snob!"

"I know, darling," she said cheerfully. "Isn't it a ghastly hoot?"

They took the car well out of the city before Quentin was prepared to change places with Immy and let her anywhere near the steering wheel. By then, she had learned where all the gears and instruments were and managed not to grip the wheel so tightly that her knuckles turned white.

It wasn't as easy as it looked, Immy admitted, and it didn't help her nerves to have her father shouting whenever the wheels approached the grass verge instead of steering a straight line down the middle of the road.

Both tempers quickly became frayed, and they had soon each had enough of it. Quentin drove them home with more speed than judgement.

"You'll have to find some other person willing to put his nerves to the test, Imogen," he told her shortly. "It's not all your fault, mind. I just don't have the patience to be a driving instructor."

"I was pretty useless all the same, wasn't I?" she said.

"Not useless. Just inexperienced, which is to be expected. Let's leave it a few weeks and perhaps we'll try again."

And perhaps they wouldn't. She was thankful Elsie had gone out to meet Joe by the time they got back so that she wouldn't have to see her crimson face. And by the time her sister came home for supper, gloomy with the news that Joe would be leaving for York the following Friday,

Immy could laugh about her first efforts at controlling a car.

She did want to learn, though, since it seemed a useful skill to acquire. There must be someone who could teach her without the two of them getting hot under the collar and screaming at one another.

Helen had owned her own small car for two years, given to her courtesy of her well-heeled father as a very special eighteenth birthday present, but Helen certainly wouldn't do as she would be far too soft as an instructor. It needed a stranger with no other interest than advising her how to keep her wheels securely on the road and assuring her she was in no danger of killing them both.

At the beginning of May, Quentin came home from the shop to say that Robert Preston seemed as capital a fellow as his cousin Joe. He had already settled in well, charming most of the shop-girls into the bargain, and Quentin thought he might ask him home for tea one Sunday afternoon.

"Do you think mixing business with pleasure is a good idea, Father?" Immy queried at once.

"Why not? Your sister doesn't object to my suggestion, so why should you? I'm sure Cook can manage to bake an extra cake or two and cut a few extra ham sandwiches. We're not inviting the king and queen, my dear."

"But he's the manager. Your boss."

"He's also a decent young man far from home, whose family sent a wreath and a genuine letter of sympathy when your mother died. The least we can do is show similar thoughtfulness, or has your generosity of spirit entirely deserted you?"

Imogen flushed to her ears. "Of course it hasn't. I was only thinking it might be a bit awkward for you and Elsie, that's all."

"Well, it won't. Besides, he particularly asked after you, and I told him you badly wanted to learn to drive a car. We decided he should teach you."

"*Father!* You didn't, did you?"

"Why on earth not? Of course I did. You can discuss it with him when you see him. Now then, I want to listen to the wireless, so go and do something else while I try and tune in to the station before the wretched battery runs out."

Imogen went off, fuming. It was bad enough that they would have to sit and be polite to Robert Preston all through a Sunday afternoon, but the thought of having to sit beside him in the close, cosy proximity of the car while he taught her to drive…his hands reaching out to correct her steering, and perhaps touching hers, by accident or design…

She knew she was letting herself become totally irrational over the whole thing, but by the time she sought out her sister, she was in a foul mood.

"You can't imagine what Father's done now, Elsie," she said furiously.

Her sister didn't look up from the hat she had brought home from work so that she could finish off the delicate stitching on its frivolous little veil.

"You're talking about Robert, I dare say," she murmured, biting off the fine thread between her teeth and inspecting her work with a critical eye, knowing the hat would make its appearance at Ascot in the summer.

"Yes. *Robert.* As well as inviting him here for tea, father's wangled it so that I have to take driving lessons with him. How *could* he have asked him? He can't possibly want to do it, and I'll be just mortified."

"Actually, it was Robert's idea. I heard him offering his services when Daddy mentioned it."

Chapter Nine

The telephone rang that evening.

They still hadn't got used to the sound of it, and invariably jumped when it happened. It was usually Aunt Rose with the weekly gossip about Teddy's doings, or how well Daisy was doing at her first aid class with her bandaging and her soothing bedside manner for the mock casualties.

There was always a faint note of surprise in her voice, which sent Imogen and Elsie off into peals of laughter when they had finished talking. Daisy with a bedside manner would be something to see – but it was the actress in her, of course, Elsie would say solemnly, which would start them off again.

"Hello," Imogen said into the telephone mouthpiece, already smiling at the expectation of chatter from her aunt.

"Am I speaking to Miss Imogen Caldwell?" she heard a deep voice say. A voice that was unmistakably northern, the flat tones even richer and more resonant over the line than they had been on the one occasion she had been face to face with their owner.

"You are," she said, unable to say more for the moment, and hoping that the wild beat of her heart wasn't as evident to him as it was to her. And why was it beating so rapidly in any case? she asked herself furiously. He was nothing to her.

"This is Robert Preston."

"I know who you are."

And for the life of her she couldn't think of anything else to say in the small pause that followed. What *did* you say at such moments?

What do you want? It was hardly polite to ask so bluntly.

Thank you for calling? That sounded like goodbye, and was also inane, since he hadn't said anything yet.

Thank you for offering to teach me to drive, but no thank you? No, because he hadn't offered it personally yet, and anyway, she knew how ungracious it would sound.

She heard a short throaty laugh at the other end.

"My, my, we are touchy, aren't we, Miss Caldwell? Have I caught you at a bad moment?"

She stared at the phone, thinking him outrageous for speaking so familiarly when she didn't even know him. Didn't *want* to know him, if the truth were told.

"Is it my father you want to speak to?" she asked in her most frigid tone.

"It's you I want," he said, and her heart gave an enormous leap in her chest, because the words were far too soft and emotive and seductive, and they scared her.

"What can I do for you?" she said, refusing to let him think she understood him all too well, and realising too late that she was leaving herself wide open with her artless words.

"It's what I can do for you, Imogen," he said.

Before she wondered whether she dared slam down the phone, since the sitting-room door was open, and the others had probably heard every word she said, he spoke more crisply.

"I understand you want to learn to drive a car, and you probably know I told your father I'd be happy to teach

152

you. But naturally it has to be your decision. The lady always has the last word."

Was there a hidden meaning in that remark? Did he mean that if he planned on seduction she could refuse and there would be no hard feelings between them?

What in heaven's name was happening to her, if she could even think such a thing? Her palms were damp as she held on to the telephone, and she was furious with herself for letting him affect her so.

"I'll think about it," she said in a strangled voice.

"Good. We'll talk about it again when I come to tea. I shall look forward to it."

She hung up before she could say any more and rejoined her father and sister in the sitting-room, hoping her cheeks weren't as fiery as they felt. Not that they would notice. Each of them was too wrapped up in their own little world to wonder what was happening to *her*… Now she was in danger of becoming paranoid, she told herself.

"That was Robert Preston," she announced, knowing they would ask. "Just wanting to know if I'd like him to teach me to drive, and I said I'd think about it."

"What's to think about?" her father said. "It'll be easier on my nerves, anyway," he added with a chuckle, before going back to his newspaper.

Elsie was engrossed in her letter from Joe, who had promised to write with devoted regularity.

"I think Robert's quite nice," she murmured without looking up. "All the lady customers think so, anyway."

I suppose you'd think it nice if we ended up having a double wedding, sister dear, Immy found herself thinking, with a shock of annoyance at her own wayward thoughts. She had no intention of falling into that trap.

Knowing more about the ways of the opposite sex than her sister, she had decided very early on that Robert Preston was one of those charismatic men who appealed to ladies of all ages – and traded on it. And she wasn't going to be one of his conquests, thank you very much.

–

"What have you got against him?" Helen said curiously.

"Nothing, I suppose. I just don't trust him."

"But you're going to let him give you driving lessons? Out in the country with a strange man?" she teased her.

"I can handle that," Immy said crossly. "And I'll *have* to agree, since my father's so keen on the idea. It's all too embarrassing!"

Helen looked thoughtful. "I think I'll pay a visit to the shop and take a look at this paragon. Elsie seems to think a lot of him, doesn't she?"

"Elsie's moping over Joe's absence, and since he and Robert virtually grew up together, I think she spends half her time pumping Robert for information about Joe's childhood. She's always coming home with some new revelation about cut knees and getting lost on the moors and stuff like that."

"Crikey, she really is besotted, isn't she?"

"That's not the word for it," Immy said drily.

"I wonder if we'll ever be that much in love with anyone. I can't see it for myself, or not for ages, anyway," Helen said, complacent in her self-sufficiency. "I'm not sure I want to be that dependent on another person's feelings, anyway. Being in love's a responsibility, isn't it?"

Immy laughed. "When did you take up philosophy – or should it be psychiatry? Are you going to start analysing me?"

"I wouldn't dare. You're far too complex for me to want to delve into your secrets, darling. Apart from the ones I know, of course."

But Helen didn't know all of them, Immy thought, as she cycled home. Helen didn't know how bitterly betrayed she had felt over Morgan, and she didn't know the depth of the turbulent feelings Robert Preston could arouse in her.

–

"You will be polite to Robert, won't you?" Elsie asked her on the Sunday he was due to come for tea.

"Why wouldn't I be?"

"Well, I know you're put out because Daddy and he seem to have cooked up the driving lessons between them, but if it's what you want, I don't see any point in getting all fussed about it. Robert's only going to be here for four weeks, so you might as well make the most of it."

Her voice implied that the sooner these four weeks were over the better, because then Joe would be back. Immy didn't miss the yearning in her voice and didn't have it in her heart to make any teasing comment about it.

"Oh well, I'm sure a couple of lessons is all I need. I do know the basics now, and then I'll be able to go wherever I like, providing Father will lend me the car. I'll be as independent as Helen."

The thought of it was starting to open up a whole new world to her. It was merely the usefulness of being able to drive that had prompted her originally, coupled with Helen's airy remark that they could both apply to be drivers for officers if war came. Her face broke into a smile as she remembered the unwittingly snobbish remark. Helen could always make her smile.

Robert Preston had clearly set out to be at his most charming when he came to the house, bearing a huge bunch of tea-roses and stephanotis that took up several vases. As the girls arranged them Immy whispered to her sister that Robert could hardly have got a more ostentatious bunch of flowers to impress them if he'd robbed a graveyard.

"Stop it; he'll hear you." Elsie grinned. "It was a lovely thought – and he's very dapper, isn't he? I know you're determined to dislike him, but if I didn't have Joe I could almost fancy him myself. You know Helen came into the shop this week, don't you? Her eyes were like saucers when she met him, and he certainly took his time showing her around the store. *More* than enough time, I'd say."

"Really?" Immy feigned as little interest as possible. She was curious and a little put out that Helen hadn't phoned her to report, though.

"So when shall we have the first lesson, Imogen? How about this evening?" Robert asked her after tea, when he had chatted with her father and quizzed Baz – at home for his regular Sunday afternoon – on his activities.

Immy's heart jolted. "So soon?"

Baz sniggered. "She'll need time to think about it, Robert. She'll be too scared of making a fool of herself."

"Of course she's not," Robert said, ignoring Immy's glare at her brother, though he was looking directly at her with his gypsy eyes. "I assure you there's no need, and I'm a very gentle teacher."

"I'm sure you are," Immy muttered.

Quentin seemed quite unaware of any undercurrents. "Take advantage of the offer, Imogen. It's what you want, isn't it?"

"And we only have a few weeks," Robert added, his gaze still unwavering, and causing that uncomfortable little leap of her heart again.

"All right. Let's get it over with," she muttered.

Her father and brother both hooted.

"Good God, girl, anyone would think you were going to the devil, instead of having a driving lesson," Quentin laughed.

"Perhaps she is," Baz sniggered again, his eyes bright and knowing.

Once she was ready for the lesson, telling herself her nerves weren't really intensified at all, Immy went into the garden to catch Baz before he returned to the Brays' cottage. Glancing around, she saw Robert still talking to her father inside the house, and she grabbed Baz's arm firmly.

"Listen to me, you little sneak. You just keep your hints to yourself, do you hear? Or I shall have to put in a few words to Father that you're getting into bad company. He's still capable of hauling you back home and changing his mind about all this ferry-boat nonsense."

He scowled at her. "All right, you don't have to make a meal of it. I was only having a bit of fun, anyway. Nobody noticed anything."

"*I* noticed, and it wasn't funny, Baz. It's never funny to make someone else feel uncomfortable. You seem to have forgotten how Mother always instilled that in us."

It was the first time they had discussed Frances since her death. He was such a toughie now, and so self-contained...but to her astonishment she saw his face suddenly twist in a look of pain, and his throat worked a little before he replied.

"It won't happen again, I promise."

"Well, that's good," she said. "The family's important, Baz. We may have separated a bit recently, but we must always stick together when it comes to basic things, family things. Mother used to say that too, before—"

"Yes, all right," he said, and from his edgy voice she knew she was going a touch too far now.

He wouldn't remember her mother's little sayings the way she did, but he would be remembering her sweet voice now, and it didn't hurt to remind him now and then that he wasn't as tough as he liked to think. She gave his shoulder a more gentle squeeze and saw him blink rapidly.

"I have to go now. I'll see you next week, sis."

He hadn't called her that for a long time, and she stared after him as he strolled jauntily down the hill towards the waterfront. He was big for his age, but he was still her little brother, and she felt unaccountably tender towards him.

"Ready?" Robert Preston's voice said behind her.

"Not really, but I suppose it's now or never," she said staunchly.

He laughed. His teeth were even and pearly white. For a totally illogical moment Imogen remembered Daisy telling her solemnly that you could tell a lot from a horse's teeth.

Did that apply to humans as well? If so, Robert Preston must be very even-tempered and very pure at heart…but she instinctively doubted both of those assessments.

"It's only a driving lesson, Immy," he said softly.

He had already cranked the engine with the starting handle, and now he opened the car door for her to get into the driving seat. She gave him a freezing look.

"I'm only Immy to my friends," she said, knowing she was being petulant, and feeling unable to help it. He simply brought out the worst in her – and this behaviour meant that her recent words to Baz had been nothing more than the pot calling the kettle the darkest shade of black.

He started to close the car door again, and she looked at him, startled.

"I refuse to teach anyone to drive while they're in a bad mood and a possible danger to others. I know fate has thrown your family and mine together, and we may not be friends. But if we can't at least be civil to one another, then we'd better forget it right now."

His eyes challenged her, and out of the corner of hers she could see her father and Elsie at the sitting-room window. She swallowed her pride with a huge effort.

"I'm sorry. I'm nervous, that's all. Of course we're friends – sort of."

He smiled again and opened the door wide. It was a bit like offering her entrance into the lion's den, Immy thought stupidly. But she slid inside the car without another word, and he closed the door before moving around to the passenger seat, enclosing them both inside. He turned to face her.

"Well then, Imogen, shall we begin? You know the procedure, I believe?"

An hour or so later Elsie was keen to hear how she had got on. By now Quentin had taken Robert off to his gentlemen's club in the city for a "well-deserved" drink or two, in his chuckling opinion.

"I managed surprisingly well," Immy said reluctantly. "He's a good teacher, I'll say that for him. I'm having another lesson on Wednesday evening, and next Sunday as well, since Father has apparently asked him for Sunday tea every week until he goes back to York."

"What did I tell you? All the Preston men are charmers, aren't they?" Elsie said happily, thinking of the only one who interested her.

"I daresay they have their charms."

"Oh Immy, you're so stubborn. Can't you ever admit you're wrong about people?"

"What do you mean?" Immy objected in genuine astonishment.

Elsie shrugged. "It's the way you are, darling. You may not realise it, but you've got some pretty rigid ideas, and nothing on earth will change them. You should take a leaf out of Daisy's book."

"What, and flit from one idea to the next as often as changing my stockings?"

"She's growing up, Immy, and she's pretty set on this nursing idea. She telephoned us while you were out, full of excitement, to say she's got an interview at the local hospital tomorrow afternoon to be taken on as a nursing auxiliary."

"Good Lord," Immy said, everything else forgotten. "I wonder how long that will last."

She caught Elsie's look, and grinned.

"All right. I'm doing it again, aren't I? I wish her luck, anyway. She's cheerful and pretty, so she'll certainly brighten up the wards if nothing else."

–

Daisy intended to do far more than that. Nursing was her vocation, she declared to her friend Lucy, advising her on gentle exercise as she tentatively put her foot to the ground to test out her sprained ankle, which had been slow to heal.

"You're a blooming doctor now, then?" Lucy said, tetchy with the boredom of inactivity, and missing her rides on Star.

"Of course not, but I probably could be," Daisy said airily. "You have to start somewhere, don't you? And once I'm taken on as an auxiliary, I'll be all ready to be sent to war when the call comes."

Lucy groaned. Having little imagination herself, she sometimes found it difficult to follow Daisy's mercurial train of thought. She herself didn't care for all the war-mongering stories gathering tempo now, either. Her life was geared to slower and steadier country ways.

"You won't catch me going to war. Me and Ben will help Dad on the farm. He says now that the government's offering farmers two pounds an acre to plough up the fields and plant more seeds for food production, we'll be laughing, anyway. Besides, war's not going to happen."

"Of course it is," Daisy said, impressed by this bit of knowledge. "Why do you think they've started conscription? Uncle Bertie says it can't be more than months away now. Oh, and did I tell you we've got two more? That's another reason why I'll be glad to start my new job."

"Two more what?"

"Infants. Evacuees. Arrived from Kent with a school supervisor, all snotty-nosed and too scared to talk, poor little squirts. Aunt Rose is in her element, and they'll be playmates for Teddy. And if *that* doesn't make it sound like there's going to be a war, I don't know what does."

"What, sending two snotty-nosed kids to live at your Aunt Rose's house to be spoiled with cake and kindness?"

"*No.* Getting them all out of London and the south-east counties ready for when the German bombs fall. Honestly, Lucy, don't you know what's going on?"

"Of course I do. Dad reads the papers and listens to the wireless all the blessed time and bores us silly with it, but I don't pay much attention to it, and I didn't think you did either."

"I didn't, but now I do," Daisy said solemnly. "You can't stay blinkered forever, can you?" She started to giggle, her sombre mood gone as quickly as it came. "Did you hear what I said just then? Blinkered! As if we were Star and Baby."

—

Immy's next three driving lessons went smoothly. She was pleasantly surprised at how patient Robert Preston could be, and how calmly she responded to his instructions after her outbursts with her father. Robert was aware of his position in the city regarding his father's business, of course, but he made no attempt to be other than polite and friendly.

If deep down that attitude mildly piqued her, Immy told herself she was being ridiculous. She didn't want his attention. She just wanted to be able to drive competently.

She reported her success to Helen, expecting her friend to be hugely approving and supportive, since she had put the idea of driving lessons into her head in the first place.

"Lucky you," was all Helen said.

"Lucky? That's an odd word to use, isn't it?"

Helen's face was a deeper colour than usual.

"I mean good for you, of course, darling."

"No, you don't. That's not what you meant, nor what you said. You said lucky me. Why lucky me?"

"You're starting to sound like a parrot, Immy."

"And you're evading the question."

"Good Lord, is this the Inquisition or something?"

Immy stared at her. They had always been able to say anything to one another, or so she thought. But there was a secretive look about Helen today, and she was definitely edgy. Immy had a sudden rush of intuition.

"Elsie says you've been to Preston's, so I know you've met him."

"Why shouldn't I? It's a shop, isn't it? People go there to buy things. I didn't think Robert Preston was your exclusive property, anyway."

"He's not! I never heard anything so daft. It's not as if I'm going *out* with him. It's only driving lessons, for heaven's sake."

She stopped, suddenly seeing all there was to see.

"You've fallen for him, haven't you? I thought you didn't believe in all that love at first sight stuff!"

"It wasn't at first sight," Helen muttered.

This took a moment longer to sink in. "Have you been *seeing* him, then? Has he asked you out?"

Helen glared at her. "You're not so pretty when you're jealous, darling. Your eyes have gone a positive shade of green. Yes, he's asked me out, and I've gone. We went to the pictures one night, if you must know, and we're going out again on Saturday night."

"I see!" Immy said, shocked.

But as Helen said, Robert Preston wasn't her exclusive property. He wasn't her property at all, nor ever likely to be. Now that the initial Heathcliff attraction had faded, she wasn't sure she even liked him all that much.

What annoyed her most was that Helen should have kept all this to herself, when they had always told one another everything – almost.

"I think it's time I went home," she said stiffly, standing up to go.

Helen capitulated at once, jumping up from her garden chair and squeezing her arm.

"Oh Immy, I would have told you, honestly. It just took me by surprise, that's all, and it – well, it scares me, I suppose. I've never felt like this before. I don't quite know what to do with the feeling."

"How very unlike you! I thought the so-sophisticated Miss Church could cope with anything."

"So did I. But I've never been in love before, and I'm not at all sure if I'm in love now. How the heck do you tell? Come on, brainbox, tell me that if you can!"

She looked so comical and bemused that Immy felt her lips twitching, and because it sounded so ridiculous they found themselves laughing helplessly together, arms around one another, practically holding one another up.

Helen's mother came into the garden, as ever the gracious hostess, a tray of lemonade and bourbons in her hands, and smiled at them indulgently.

"Now then, you two girls, what wicked little schemes are you planning today?" she enquired, serenely sure there could be no undesirable secrets between her dutiful, sweet-faced daughter and her lovely friend.

At which the two of them became convulsed all over again.

Chapter Ten

Robert Preston had no intention of seducing the Caldwell girl. It had only ever been a passing thought, since she was the most alluring of the bunch. But he liked them more pliant, and Imogen Caldwell was far too strong-willed for him to take on. In any case, he was far too aware of his position to get caught up in that little trap. Desirable as she was to any red-blooded man with heat in his loins – and he was certainly that – she was a canny lass who would read him like a book. And she was still the daughter of a small-time shopkeeper.

His cousin Joe was more liberal-minded than he was in that respect, and if he wanted to dally with the other one, it was his affair. Robert himself had ambitions of a higher order, however. He had the smouldering looks and his father's go-getting personality, and he had proved on plenty of occasions that he could get any girl he wanted. And right now, he wanted Helen Church.

He felt a tingling in his nether regions just thinking about her, but he hadn't made his real move yet. He was sure she was a virgin, and therefore he had to go slowly if he didn't want to frighten her off.

Her classy, non-Bristol accent and her well-heeled connections were the main attraction, of course. Robert's father was a self-made man with a bluff and gritty Yorkshire exterior, and a girl with a bit of class had always appealed to Robert. Not least because he revelled in the triumphant idea that his wild gypsy looks could always tame them.

There was one insurmountable problem regarding Helen Church, though. He had to be back in York at the end of May, and there simply wasn't the time available to woo her as slowly as he knew was wise.

But the more he thought about her, the more he ached to have her. So if he was to make a conquest, the only way was to overwhelm her with charm and seduction and a profusion of small, acceptable gifts. And now it was time for the kill.

–

He took her for a drive in the country on Saturday evening, and eventually parked his car in a secluded copse well away from the city. He turned to Helen and handed her a small gift-wrapped box.

She accepted it with a squeal of delight. She wasn't unused to receiving expensive presents from her parents, and occasionally her brother James could surprise her with something unusual and exotic, but Robert's selection of gifts had been very sweet so far. A china dog for her bedroom; a hair-tidy; a box of Turkish Delight; a discreet bottle of lavender-water; nothing to which her parents could object.

But before today she had never in her life received anything from a young man – other than her brother, who didn't count – that came in a jeweller's box.

It had to mean something. It had to mean he was falling as headlong in love with her as she as with him. She was dizzy with the thought, and she opened the box and took out the glittering crystal pendant with shaking hands.

"Oh, Robert, it's beautiful," she breathed.

"So are you," he said, his voice thickening. He caught her hands in his, and the trail of gold chain draped over them both, enclosing the crystal. It was symbolic, Helen thought dreamily, as besotted with love as Elsie Caldwell.

"I wonder if you know just how beautiful you are, Helen, and just how much you tantalise a man."

"Tantalise you?" she protested with a shivery laugh. "I don't mean to do any such thing!"

"But you do. You make me want to do things I've never done with anyone before," he said, so convincingly that she could do nothing but believe him as his dark eyes bored intensely into hers.

She ached with love for him, and it had happened so suddenly, so amazingly and spectacularly suddenly, that she couldn't think straight. Couldn't sleep without dreaming of him. Couldn't eat.

He took the slender chain out of her hands and she leaned forward as he fastened it around her throat. It lay shimmering against her pale skin, and he bent and kissed it.

Her heart pounded as she wondered fleetingly what her mother's reaction to such a gift from a young man would be. It was terribly personal. Too personal, by her mother's strict reckoning.

But it was becoming difficult to concentrate on anything other than Robert's hands, warm on her body, caressing her breasts and sending exquisite shooting sensations right through her. All her senses were alive to his touch and the wickedness of it all…the shameful, delicious, decadent wickedness…

He was unfastening the buttons on her afternoon frock so gently and skilfully that she hardly noticed it, nor realised that his lips were moving downwards over her skin. She was simply drowning in the new sensation... Suddenly she was frightened as she felt his hand slide inside the bodice of her frock. His fingers squeezed her nipple, and she heard his breathing quicken.

"No. Don't. Robert, please," she appealed.

"*Please* is what I want to hear. A bit of begging is as good as sweet music. Be nice to me, lass," he whispered.

"I didn't mean that. Please don't do it, Robert."

But he wasn't listening to her. It was now or never, and the ache in his loins was too great to be denied. He tugged her breast out of its confining bodice and his mouth fastened over her nipple, his tongue caressing and tasting, and whipping up more of these strange sensations in her that she didn't understand and knew she didn't want.

They were too powerful. Uncontrollable. And she had never lost control of her own emotions before. The feeling of alarm far outweighed the dizzying sense of pleasure his touch had evoked. She was also sick with furious embarrassment, knowing now that he had expected this as a reward for his gift. Any thoughts of love vanished as quickly as they had come, and, in her mind, he was an animal slavering over her.

She jerked away from him, scarlet with shame at the sight of her own breast exposed to the daylight, with the slickness of his tongue still on it.

She covered herself quickly and spoke through shuddering lips. "Take me home, please. And give this to someone who will be glad to pay in kind for your generosity."

She wrenched the pendant from her throat, uncaring that the clasp of the chain broke. It was as tawdry as she felt.

"There's a name for girls like you," Robert snarled, sparks of anger lighting his eyes. "You're worse than a street tart. At least they ply their trade honestly and don't tease a man to death."

"I never tried to tease you," Helen almost sobbed. "I thought you liked me. I thought you *loved* me."

He heard the catch in her throat and sensed the romantic idealism of a girl not yet schooled in lust. His attitude gentled again until he was as seductive as a panther stalking its prey.

"Well, my lovely girl, isn't that exactly what I want to do if you'll let me?"

He wasn't giving up just yet, not while she had soft tears brimming in her eyes, and her lips trembled so enticingly. He let his hand rest on her knee over her silky skirt, stroking her upper leg with imperceptible movements, and pressed his cheek to hers as he felt her relax again.

"Love means trusting another person, lass," he whispered, his mouth on hers now. "You can trust me not to hurt you."

She didn't understand what he meant until she felt the heat of his hand beneath her skirt and the harder pressure of it. Felt it sliding quickly upwards and inwards as his breath hoarsened again, and she could smell the lust in him.

Helen was gripped by fear, but she couldn't let this happen. *Wouldn't* let it happen. With an instinct stronger than fear she clamped her knees together and rammed her fist into his face with all her strength.

"You little vixen," Robert yelled. He let go of her at once as he reeled back in the car to clutch at his nose. His elegant nose, that had a streak of blood coming from it now...

"If you don't take me home this minute, I shall get out of this car and start running," Helen screamed, even though she had no idea where they were. "I shall shriek rape to anyone within hearing distance, and we'll see what all your fancy clothes and your daddy's reputation does for you then!"

"And who do you think will believe you?" But his sneer was fast becoming a bluster, and all his fight and libido was shrivelling as he saw the cold fury in her eyes.

Bloody *class* did this, he found himself thinking furiously, the breeding that was denied to his sort. She would never be persuaded into the hay. She had iron control when it was needed, and she had it now. The bitch had dragged it up from somewhere.

"Who would believe you?" he snapped again, when she had stared him out, unnerving him even more.

"Anyone who sees this," Helen snapped back, and calmly ripped the bodice of her best Sunday frock as if it was tissue paper. He supposed it was of no consequence to a girl whose father could always buy her more. "Now drive me home. Providing I get home with no one seeing me, I'll forget this ever happened. Except that I always confide everything to my best friend."

He stared at her in shocked disbelief, his face a picture of impotent rage. "You surely don't mean Imogen Caldwell?"

"The very same," Helen said grimly, knowing she had the upper hand now, and aware that several other cars were in the vicinity on this lovely evening. If she chose to shout for help, there was nothing else Robert Preston could do to her now, without others being aware of it.

They drove back to her house at speed, and in total silence. Helen thanked her stars that her parents were away for the night and wouldn't witness her humiliation. Nor would she be obliged to explain her disgraceful appearance to them.

She slammed the car door in a final gesture of defiance and heard Robert curse before he drove off in a temper.

Only then, when she was safely indoors and alone, did her knees buckle, and she leaned against her own front door with tears streaming down her face.

"What a fool. What a mad, bloody fool I was to be so taken in by looks and smooth talking," she finally whispered savagely into the empty house. She never swore in anger and hated him still more for reducing her to it.

She went to the ornate bathroom her father had had installed and stripped off every bit of clothing while she filled the bath with hot water. Then she scrubbed every inch of her body and soaked herself for half an hour, until the water ran cool and her skin was wrinkled and alabaster white but bore no more traces of Robert Preston's touch.

Finally, with no more tears left to weep, she put on an everyday frock and systematically destroyed every single thing he had bought her. Only then did she feel moderately cleansed. And only then did she realise that she couldn't bear to be alone any longer.

There was only one person she needed. Only one other person who would understand. She called her on the telephone, praying she would be the one to answer.

"Immy, I need to see you right away," she croaked.

The shock in her voice transmitted itself at once.

"Where? Do you want me to come to you, Helen?"

"*No.* Somewhere out of doors. I'll drive to the park near you and meet you there in ten minutes. I have to talk to you. I feel" – she gulped – "so dirty."

"I'll be right there," Immy said. "Whatever it is, we can sort it out, Helen."

A sixth sense told her exactly what she was going to hear. She left Vicarage Street and walked quickly to the grassy park, which was busy with parents and children on a balmy evening, telling herself not to condemn. Not to be an I-told-you-so friend. Telling herself she could be wrong, and probably was.

One look at Helen's feverish face told her she was not. She took her friend's hand tightly in her own, and they sat on a park bench near the pond in the shade of one of the graceful weeping willows. It seemed ominously appropriate.

"Was it Robert?" she asked quietly.

Helen was brittle with hurt and lashed out at once.

"How did you know? Did he try it with you too? Why didn't you warn me? You *should* have warned me, Immy."

"I didn't know, and he didn't try it with me – and I'm only guessing, darling. Tell me what happened."

Apart from any physical hurt, it wasn't hard for Immy to see what the experience had done to her friend. The old confident Helen had temporarily gone, and in her place was a terrified girl who had seen something far uglier than she had known before. Helen would have thought it all a delicious game, and now she knew it was not. You didn't play with fire and not expect to get burnt. The trouble was, Helen did.

"Helen, he didn't..." Immy's voice sharpened. "You know it's a criminal offence for a man to force himself on you, and your father would take him all the way—"

"My father's not to hear a word of this," Helen stuttered. "Nobody but you, Immy. Promise me. *Please.*"

"Of course I promise, if you're sure you weren't hurt."

"He didn't rape me. I know that's what you're thinking, and you'll probably think I'm making far too much of it all. But I was so *scared*, Immy. I can't tell you how scared I was, and if that's what love is, I want no more of it."

She shuddered a breath. "Not that it was love on his part, nor mine. I was just infatuated. A stupid, pathetic girl who got her head turned. But not anymore. I hate him now."

Immy knew she had to tread carefully. There was a time for an intimate discussion about the difference between love and lust, and it wasn't now.

"What exactly did he do, Helen? Just between us. It *is* why you called me, isn't it? To unburden yourself?"

"Yes," Helen muttered, drawing another deep breath. "Oh, it all seems so silly now. But it was so sordid at the time."

She described it quickly, her face as hot as fire as she did so. Immy slid an arm around her friend's shoulders, feeling the tension in her whole body.

"I know you won't believe me right now, but love...it's not as awful as it seems, Helen. At least, it won't be when you find the right man. You have to know that. He was only after one thing, but they're not all the same."

"What about your MR? You thought he was the right one, didn't you? How does anybody know?"

Helen's eyes burned with aggression, prepared to argue with anyone, and although Immy tried to placate her she still wasn't calm by the time the air grew chilly and the park had become more or less deserted except for themselves.

She came to a decision. "Helen, I'm going to take you home and make us some hot cocoa, and then I'm going to call my father and tell him I'm staying the night with you because your parents are away. Is that all right?"

Helen's voice was husky with relief. She wilted against her friend. "It's more than all right. You're the best pal, Immy, and I'm an idiot to be making such a fuss."

"No, you're not. You've had a shock, but I bet we'll be laughing about it tomorrow."

She doubted it, and her head pounded with the irrational thought that the responsibility for this all harked back to the Caldwells.

If her father and Elsie hadn't gone to work for the Prestons and invited Robert home, and if *she* hadn't talked about him more than she realised, Helen would never have been agog to see this wonder man – and then entered into a kind of unspoken rivalry with Immy. They both knew about that one, even though neither of them ever voiced it.

"I'm not sure I can even drive home. My hands are shaking too much," Helen said abruptly when they reached the road where her small car was parked.

"You don't have to. I'm a driver now, remember? If you'll trust me with your car, of course."

"You're the only one I do trust," Helen said, and they both knew she wasn't just talking about the car.

It wasn't familiar, but a car was just a car, Immy told herself, and by the time they reached Helen's house, with a few jerks and false starts and under-the-breath curses, she knew there would be no more driving lessons with Robert Preston.

It would be her father or Helen. Or nothing. But that was for later. They had to get through this night, and tomorrow there were other things to sort out. Helen wasn't the only one who was a crusader when the need arose, she thought grimly.

–

Helen's parents were due home during Sunday morning, and if she wasn't exactly laughing by the time Imogen left, the first shock had faded, and she was viewing things more calmly.

Immy knew which hotel Robert was staying at, and she had no qualms about marching into the foyer and asking the receptionist to let him know she wished to see him.

"Whom shall I say is calling, madam?" the man said, his eyebrows marginally raised at the sight of a young lady with hair like fire and eyes like fury entering the hotel unaccompanied in the middle of a Sunday morning.

"Miss Imogen Caldwell," she said coolly. "And it's a matter of urgency, if you please."

She wasn't intimidated by the air of superiority all these people assumed. They worked for a salary, the same as she did. She waited unblinkingly while he contacted Robert's room on an internal telephone.

"Mr Preston will be down shortly, Miss Caldwell. If you would care to wait in the lounge."

"I'll wait in the garden," she told him, having already assessed the tables and chairs under shady umbrellas for guests' use. She suspected that what she had to say would be less likely to be overheard outside than inside.

She had to wait a good ten minutes before he appeared, which did nothing to cool her temper. She stared at him without speaking, resisting any reaction or comment as she saw the darkening bruise around his nose and beneath his eye. Helen had done a good job.

"I had a fall," he said abruptly.

"No, you didn't. You were punched by a young lady resisting your unwanted advances," she said deliberately.

"Keep your voice down, for God's sake," he hissed.

Seeing the hunted way he glanced around, Imogen sat back, knowing she was going to make the most of this, and intending to make him cringe until he wished himself back in Yorkshire.

"It was my intention to do so, and also the reason I suggested meeting in the garden. But now I'm not so sure I want to keep quiet about the kind of man you are. The kind who is outwardly a pillar of society, who charms all the elderly ladies who come into his store, but who sees fit to lure naïve young girls into the country and then tries to seduce them."

"My God, who are you, the Virgin Mary? It wasn't like that, anyway," Robert blustered. "And she's not naïve. She knows what it's all about."

"Helen Church is the sweetest girl I know, and she certainly does *not* know what it's all about, as you so crudely put it. By the way, did you know her father's an eminent solicitor in this city?"

It was sweet to see him blanch. He had an outdoor, rugged complexion, but it went an unattractive sickly yellow at that moment.

"She's not telling him, is she? My God, Imogen, you've got to stop her. My reputation is at stake!"

"Your reputation is that of a river-rat – it stinks," Immy told him coldly. "And we haven't decided whether or not to tell her father yet."

"*We?* You don't know what actually happened, do you?" He tried to bluff it out now. "You weren't there.

All this fuss over a few kisses! It's only a stupid girl's word, and none of your damn business, anyway."

"You bastard!" Immy said in a low vibrant voice. "You despicable *bastard*."

Her violent reaction shocked him. She shocked herself, but she was too incensed on Helen's behalf to care.

"I *do* know what happened, because when she got home Helen called me in a terrible state and I spent all night at her house, listening to her and comforting her."

"Over a few kisses?" he sneered.

"Over what would be construed in a court of law as attempted rape."

She had him now. She could see it by the way his knuckles whitened, his fingernails biting so hard into his palms they would surely draw blood eventually. She could see it by the way the pulse in his throat throbbed as if it would burst, and by the way the veins in his forehead stood out like purple ropes. He was scared stiff, and she was *glad*.

She stood up, smoothing down the skirt of her frock with hands that trembled slightly. Now that it was almost done, she felt faint, but she wasn't going to let him see it.

"One more thing. I want no more driving lessons from you, and you will not come to tea with us again. You will make whatever excuse you like to my father, but if you set one foot inside my house again, I shall have no alternative but to tell my father everything."

"I can hardly avoid seeing him at the shop!"

"The shop is a different matter – and, thank God, you'll be leaving it soon. If there are any more arrangements about exchanging managers, please ensure that you don't come back to Bristol again. I won't have you violating my mother's house with your presence. We're a decent family, and we don't take kindly to scum. Have I made myself clear?"

"Perfectly," he snarled. "And I was right. You are the bloody Virgin Mary. So do you want to shake on it?"

He oozed sarcasm, adding blasphemy to everything else. He held out his hand to her, and she took a pace backwards.

"I wouldn't touch you if you were the last man on earth," she said vehemently.

—

No one glancing out of an upper window of the hotel could have resisted a comment about Imogen Caldwell's hair, its sheen caught in the glow of morning sunlight that turned it to a blaze of fire.

The chambermaid sighed enviously to her older companion as they stripped the sheets and pillowcases off the bed, ready for laundering.

"Wish I had hair like that, don't you, Lizzie? My boy likes red hair. Says it goes with a hot nature, if you get my meaning," she added with a giggle.

"I don't know nothing about that, but I reckon the bloke with the funny way of talking's a bit of all right. You know who she is, don't you?"

"Never seen her before."

"Yes you have, ninny. She's one of them Caldwell girls. Family fell on hard times 'til they started working in that new emporium. Bit of a come-down for the father, of course. The mother fell off the cliffs last year. *You* know. But did she fall or was she pushed?" Lizzie commented sagely.

As Dolly looked blank, she went on irritably. "I been watching them two down there and all, and I reckon there's a lot of summat going on."

"Is there? I only noticed her hair."

"That's because you're too dozy to notice anything that's not spelled out for you. Well, you'd best start noticing this bedding before you get a rollicking from the housekeeper for idling and stop getting cow-eyed over the nobs."

Dolly would forget all about the little scene within minutes, Lizzie thought, but *she* wouldn't. Not when she had a tasty titbit of news to tell her sister, who cleaned at the newspaper offices, about how one of them haughty Caldwell girls had spent half the morning in the company of a guest at the hotel.

Sunday morning, too, when you might have expected a family like hers to be at church. Not the toff, though. Working at the hotel as long as she had, Lizzie had seen all sorts, and knew a thing or two about men.

This one had wicked eyes and a flat way of talking in that come-hither voice of his, and he called her "lass", which made her feel quite young again. She had smelled the stuff in his bathroom – which was a bit poncy for a man, in Lizzie's opinion – and had looked through his dressing-table drawers. She'd seen the saucy magazines he read, which had made her eyebrows rise a little.

But he wasn't above sharing a joke and having a bit of a laugh, slapping her backside playfully when she did his room and tossing her a few coins for her trouble.

She had a fair idea about that nasty bruise around his eye this morning, too. She'd seen a few of them in her time. Maybe that was also down to the Caldwell girl. Lizzie wasn't above elaborating a bit when it came to telling a good tale about the goings-on in the hotel business and getting an extra half-pint of stout for her trouble.

With her imagination, she sometimes reckoned she could have been writing some of them penny dreadfuls, she thought cheerfully. *And* writing them better!

Chapter Eleven

It was late in the evening when Quentin Caldwell came back to the sitting-room where his two daughters had just closed the books they were reading and decided it really was time they were in bed.

"What an extraordinary thing," he said to them. "I can't quite make head nor tail of it, but I've just had Owen Preston calling me all the way from Yorkshire on the telephone to say I'll be temporarily in charge of the shop as of tomorrow."

"*You?*" Elsie said in astonishment. "But why?"

"I do have managerial experience, Elsie," he said drily.

"I didn't mean that, Daddy. But what about Robert? He won't like it at all, and it's going to put his nose right out of joint, isn't it?"

Imogen kept her face as immobile as she could, thinking that Helen had already done that, and that although Robert's nose was the least of his worries, it too would take some explaining to his father, if what she suspected was happening.

The next minute she knew her intuition was right.

"It seems that Robert is required in York and has to be back there right away. I've no idea of the reason, and it wasn't my place to ask. Owen seemed brusque enough as it was."

He smiled archly at his second daughter. "Aren't you going to ask the next question?"

"I don't know. Am I?" Elsie's face suddenly flooded with colour, and Immy saw how radiantly beautiful she was when thoughts of her young man filled her mind.

"Oh, *does* this mean Joe will be coming back sooner than expected?" she asked, clasping her hands excitedly.

"It does. I'm in full charge only for a short time. Joe will be back at the end of the week, so you'll probably see him on Sunday. He and I will have plenty to discuss."

Immy cleared her throat. "Father, I wonder if this would be a good time to ask you a special favour, since you're in such a good mood."

"Well, you can always ask, and I can always say no," he added, teasing her.

But he was indulgent, with the way things were going. Robert was a good fellow, but lately he had become a bit too pompous and sure of himself. Power didn't suit everyone and, like his daughter, Quentin much preferred Joe.

"I hope you'll say yes! It's about the car."

"What about the car? The last time I saw it I believe it was all in one piece."

Immy mentally gritted her teeth at having to say the next bit but knew there was no other way.

"Robert says I've done very well, and he thinks I should do some solo driving now to get proper experience, so I was wondering if I could borrow it on Sunday. I'll be very careful with it and go out in the country where there won't be any traffic. What do you think?"

Quentin didn't say anything for a minute, but Immy desperately hoped he would agree. She might even ask Helen to accompany her, to take her out of herself...but that would defeat the object. She needed that feeling of total independence.

"I don't see why not, but if that's to be the way of things, you'd better start saving up to buy one of your own, miss. And don't pick up any strangers," her father said with a smile, sure that she wouldn't.

"Oh, Immy would never do that," Elsie said, in a rosy glow at the thought of Joe coming back. "She's far too sensible. No stranger would dare to take advantage of *her*!"

"Good Lord, what a dreary image you have of me!" Immy said, not at all pleased at the thought that she was being compared to a dragon lady. "You make me sound as middle aged as the Marys upstairs."

Among themselves, they had taken to referring to the quiet widows in the apartment upstairs as "the Marys", after discovering they both shared the same first name. It brought a smile to Immy's face, and Elsie laughed.

"No one could ever accuse you of being middle aged, Immy, nor dreary. All I meant was that you're far too intelligent to be taken in by people, and it's something to be admired."

Immy couldn't argue with that, though it had taken her a while to see through Robert Preston, she admitted. But now that he was in the past, she could forget him.

–

Lizzie Reed's sister Meg worked as a cleaner in the news-paper office and was keen to pass on the bit of gossip she had heard about the handsome Yorkshire bloke who had been in charge of Preston's Emporium for such a short time.

"Ever so good looking he was, according to our Lizzie," her sister said with a sigh.

"Your Lizzie would think anything in trousers was good looking," her fellow cleaner grinned.

"That's true, but she always says it pays to be nice to people in her line of work, and before the bloke left the hotel he gave her a good tip for her trouble."

"Oh, yes; and what kind of trouble was that, then?" the other woman sniggered.

"I think it included keeping her mouth shut about certain goings-on," Meg said, lowering her voice. "But between you and me, it had a bit to do with that Caldwell girl. You know the one I mean. The snooty one. Don't work at the shop no more but went up in the world with her office typing, so they say."

"You mean the one with the funny name? Imogen or summat?"

Meg nodded. "That's her. She ain't so snooty that she can't chase after a man, though. Lizzie says she seen 'er with him at the hotel early on Sunday morning, so tell me that ain't saucy if you like! They was having a right old barney in the garden, and Lizzie reckons he was giving her the brush-off and she was pleading with him to stay."

"Blimey. You wouldn't catch me pleadin' with a bloke."

"Nor me," Meg said. "Unless he was as loaded as that one. I might be tempted then."

They laughed bawdily together as they got on with their floor cleaning. At that moment a junior reporter took a batch of papers into the print room.

"I've just heard a spicy bit of gossip that might interest you," he said to the smooth-talking Welshman working there, hoping it might boost his status.

"I doubt that," said Morgan Raine, with undisguised loathing for the little sneak. He'd probably make a good reporter someday, though, he acknowledged, since his nasty little ear was always to the ground for anything sleazy.

"Didn't you do some advertising leaflets for one of those Caldwell girls, whose father used to have his own shop before he went down in the world?" Davy Batt went on, hiding his resentment at the way Morgan always looked down on him.

He'd caught Morgan's attention now. He was presumably referring to the second daughter, but Morgan instantly recalled the times he'd had with Imogen. He remembered her with a lustful yearning, and more than once he had wished he'd never done the dirty on her. She had been a sparky little thing; his new girl was nowhere near as responsive in certain quarters.

"This had better be good. You're running down a family who've had a rotten share of bad luck recently," he snapped as the idiot fidgeted from one foot to the other.

"The one I'm talking about is the other one. The oldest one. Some call her the snooty one."

Morgan's heart jolted.

"Imogen Caldwell? What about her, you loon?" he said sharply, forgetting he wasn't supposed to know her.

Davy Batt knew he wouldn't get anywhere unless he came out with it. He spoke more boldly.

"She was with one of them Yorkshire fellows in some posh hotel early on Sunday morning. Don't that make for a juicy bit of gossip?"

One second Morgan couldn't believe what he was hearing. The next, he had caught the boy by the throat and was twisting his flesh in his hands.

"You lying little bastard," he hissed.

"I ain't lying!" he choked. "Ask them cleaning women if you don't believe me. It's them spreading the gossip."

"And you're adding to it, you toe-rag," Morgan grated, letting him go so fast that he staggered back. "Get out of here before I throw you out."

Davy dashed for the door, turning to yell back at Morgan when he was out of arm's length.

"Bloody Welsh turd. Go back to the bloody land of your fathers – if you know which one is yours."

"What in God's name's going on here?" Morgan heard his boss say above the rattle of the machinery. By then, however, he was out looking for the cleaning women. He found them leaving after their morning session with their mops and buckets.

"Which of you is spreading wicked lies about Imogen Caldwell?" he demanded.

"'Tain't lies, Welshy," Meg said at once. "My sister seen 'em canoodling in the hotel where the gent was staying. I'd say she'd been staying there too, if you get my meaning."

Her sly wink incensed Morgan so much that he had a job to keep his hands off her, except that she smelled of carbolic and bleach and stale clothes.

"Miss Caldwell has a respectable home and family, and if you repeat any more of this I'll have you up for slander – and your sister too," he ranted.

"Here, I didn't mean nothing by it," Meg said, scared by the look in his eyes. "It was just summat my sister said."

"Well, tell your sister to mind what she says in future, because it can have serious repercussions."

He doubted that she knew the meaning of the word, but his tone was enough to scare her still more. Her companion nudged her and said they'd better be off, or they'd miss their bus.

"I won't say no more about it, then," Meg said at last, "and I'll tell Lizzie she was prob'ly wrong. Will that do?"

"It'll have to," Morgan said.

He turned away, but not soon enough to miss hearing Meg tell the other one that she knew Lizzie wasn't damn well wrong, and that one with the fancy name was prob'ly no better than she ought to be.

Which was a damn silly phrase if he ever heard one, Morgan fumed, still not too sure why he was so het up over Imogen's reputation. She was nothing to him anymore – though she could have been, if only he hadn't been so careless in walking out with another girl on that Sunday afternoon last year.

Well, it was a long time ago now, and the dust had settled by now. But the need to see her again came over him with an urgency that took him by surprise.

"You'll never guess who came into the shop today," Elsie told her sister after work the following evening.

"I don't know. Surprise me," Immy said with a smile.

"That young man who did the leaflets for me – and that was a waste of money, because I never did work at home."

"What did he want?" Immy broke in, realising from the faraway look in Elsie's eyes that she was going to start musing that if she had worked at home, she would never have had the opportunity to see Joe every single day.

"What did who want? Oh, that man. He was asking after you, and I must say, Immy, he sounded rather keen. You said he was only an acquaintance, but he made it sound as if you were more than that. Have you been keeping things from me all this time?" she teased, clearly not really believing it.

"Certainly not," Immy said crossly. "He is – *was* – only an acquaintance, and I haven't seen him in months. I can't think why he would have asked after me."

She ignored her erratic heart beats, thinking guiltily that Morgan Raine had been far, far more than a mere acquaintance. More than a friend, or a sweetheart. He had been the love of her life, as she had been his…or so she had thought, until he had shattered those illusions.

"Anyway, when he asked what you were doing these days—"

"Elsie, you didn't tell him, did you?"

"I didn't think it was a secret. He could have walked into your office any day of the week and seen you there. People visit a housing agent's office all the time. And why are you getting so cross with me?"

Immy tried to calm down. It wasn't Elsie's fault that she was so sweetly and innocently involved with Joe and had no idea of the dark forces raging inside her sister's head right now. And not just in her head, either.

"I'm not cross with you," she said. "It was just the surprise of hearing you mention him again, that's all."

"Well, if that's your reaction to an old acquaintance turning up, I dread to think what an old boyfriend might do."

Elsie started to laugh, and then saw the momentarily unguarded expression on Immy's face.

"My heavens, that's it, isn't it? You knew him far better than you let on. And you never told me!"

Since that last fact seemed to be the sum total of her indignation, Immy managed to laugh it off.

"That's because there was absolutely nothing to tell. I knew him for a few weeks, and we hit it off rather well before we went our separate ways. And now I'm going to bed!"

She needed to be alone, to try to slow down her hammering heart, and to forget all the memories Elsie had so unwittingly brought to life.

But as she undressed quickly and slid between the cool sheets, she couldn't rid her thoughts of that one phrase, "We hit it off rather well."

She closed her eyes in the soft darkness of her bedroom and remembered all too vividly how wonderful it had been before all her girlish dreams had been destroyed.

She had loved him with all the passion of first love, trusting in his words, in his deep, lilting Welsh voice, in his sensuous touch that could arouse her in a way she had never known before. She shivered, curling into a ball in her cotton nightgown, hugging her body tight, and remembering just how magical it had been.

She had awoken to his kisses and his love like a flower opening in the sun, wanting him, welcoming him, ripe and ready to take the next step, no matter how she had tried to deny it to herself, and to Helen…and it had all been so loving and so different from the crude way Robert Preston had tried to force himself on her friend.

Her thoughts shifted again. She remembered that awful night when Helen had called for her help, and her eyes flew open now, staring up into the darkness.

Morgan had never been like that, but she was older and wiser now, and who knew whether a gentle seduction was any the less a violation than the crudest kind? How could you tell?

She moved restlessly in her bed, turning to watch the patterns of moonlight dappling the curtains of her room as the breeze scurried through the trees outside. Wondering if she would ever have taken that final step if Morgan had asked her and knowing in her heart that she would.

Love would have made her accept that it was the natural thing to do. Love, and the persuasion of a lover skilled in the ways of seduction. And even the thought that she would have given in so gladly made her wicked. Wanton. As bad as any waterfront street-woman. And she was thankful that she had never been put to the test after all.

–

She looked up from the letter she was typing the following afternoon with her usual professional smile, expecting to see a client. Then her heart jumped into her throat.

"Hello, cariad," said Morgan softly, using the Welsh word for "darling" that had always sent delicious shivery feelings shooting through her. This time, however, she refused to let them in.

"What do you want?" she stammered, angry with herself for behaving in this way, for being reduced to a schoolgirl again, just because he had the same dark brooding look he had always had. Even the sight of his smiling mouth could remind her of his kisses, and how she had always wanted more...

She struggled to remember where she was, and who she was, and that he had betrayed her.

"We need to talk, Immy," he said quietly.

"We don't have anything to say to one another."

"It's important. But not here. Perhaps on Sunday."

"I shan't be here on Sunday. I have to go somewhere."

It gave her a childish satisfaction to say it, to not be readily available whenever he chose to drop by. And then she went and ruined it all.

"I could manage tomorrow afternoon if it's *really* important, though I can't imagine that you have anything to say that will interest me."

"Trust me, Immy, it's something you'll want to hear. Where, then?"

Up on the hill, in our favourite hollow? She could almost hear the words leaving his lips and knew she couldn't bear to hear them. It would be too emotional, and she wasn't sure she was ready to have her heart opened again.

And to trust him...? She had done that once before and look where it had got her.

"I'll meet you for a few minutes in the park, near the lake," she said quickly. "I can be there about three o'clock. If that's no good, I'm sorry—"

"It's perfect. And Immy, you look wonderful. I'd forgotten just how lovely you are."

"Tomorrow, then," she said quickly, not wanting this. "But I shan't be able to stay long."

She was still staring into space when her employer came out to the reception area from his own office. He was forty, sandy-haired, pudding-faced and kindly, and very partial to having such a "vibrant" young lady fronting his establishment. He used the word as often as he could, hoping that the ungrammatical but transatlantic sound of it proved that he was up to the minute and not as fuddy-duddy as his appearance might suggest. *Did* suggest, he thought mournfully.

"Are you all right, Imogen?" he said, suddenly struck by her stillness. He was used to hearing the clatter of the typewriter keys whenever he came to speak to her.

"I think so. Yes, of course I am." She realised what she was saying, and where she was. "Sorry, Mr Harris. I was dreaming. I'll get back to work right away."

He put a fatherly hand on her shoulder, even though he had begun to feel anything but fatherly towards her. But he would never have said anything about his feelings. In any case, they were not the feelings of a typical Romeo. He had always known he was lacking in the passion department, and it had relieved rather than concerned him. Caring and devotion were something else, however.

He had devoted his life to his mother until her death, and he would have devoted it to any woman who cared for him in a calm and platonic way with few other obligations. But most women wouldn't want that, especially not this one. He knew well enough that Imogen Caldwell was not for him. Not this lovely, vivacious young woman who could surely have any young man she wanted – and who, curiously enough, had never mentioned one.

Most gossipy young women couldn't resist talking about their sweethearts to anyone who would listen, but in his eyes that was another thing that set her apart from the rest. She was unique. She was his Imogen, his shining star, his humble slave – even though he was her employer and paid her wages – and he was content just to see her every day.

"Shall I put the kettle on?" he heard her say.

He blinked and turned away, as if afraid she might be able to see into his soul.

"Please do, my dear. I feel the need for sustenance."

Immy always thought him a bit eccentric with his frequently pompous way of talking, but she always felt safe with him. He was like a father figure or a favourite uncle.

In the tiny cupboard that passed for a kitchen area, she filled the kettle with cold water and lit the gas ring with a match, then put two cups and saucers on the tin tray he had brought back from a long-ago holiday in Cornwall with his mother. They were adorned with pictures of tin mines and pixies, the ruins of Tintagel Castle, and strange words in the Cornish language all around the rim.

Immy deliberately dissected her employer's character all the while she prepared the tea and biscuits, simply to keep her mind off the man whose image was really claiming her thoughts. She veered off Morgan and concentrated on Kenneth Harris.

Sometimes she couldn't make him out. She knew he had never been married. Nor was he particularly attractive, though she supposed he was the kind of man some women might want to mother. Now nobody would ever say that about Morgan...

She sighed, giving up the attempt to keep him out of her mind. She didn't want to think of him, but she had arranged to meet him, and she wouldn't go back on that. Whatever he had to say, she would tell him firmly that this was the last time. She wouldn't risk her heart being broken for a second time. It was why she had suggested they meet openly in the park. Let him say what he had to say and that would be the end of it.

–

"I hope you know what you're doing, darling," Helen said, when she reported the news to her that evening.

They were sitting in the Churches' fragrant garden as usual. It was a tribute to Helen's mother's green fingers. Right now it was a profusion of heavenly scented roses, tobacco plants and the delicate perfume of honeysuckle, and was alive with the contented hum of summer bees.

On such an evening, how could anyone ever imagine that war was on the horizon, or that the tranquillity of

England could ever be decimated again, the way it had been twenty-five years before?

The thought flitted in and out of Immy's head as she tried to concentrate on what Helen was saying.

"Whatever he wants, I'm going to make it perfectly clear that I don't want to see him again."

"So why did you say you'd see him at all?"

"I don't know. It sounded important, that's all. Or perhaps I want to prove once and for all that I can meet him socially, and that he means nothing to me anymore."

"Is that the truth?"

"I want it to be," Immy said honestly. "I know I can never feel the same way about him again. I could never trust him, Helen, and without trust, it wouldn't work. You have to be able to trust a man. You know what I mean, don't you?"

"You don't have to ask me that," Helen said. "It will be a long time before I trust anyone again."

"But you will in time. We both will. Anyway, let's forget Robert Preston – and MR, too. How's James? Have you heard from him recently? It seems ages since I saw him."

"He's transferred to the Tank Corps. God knows why, but I think it's some mannish thing. Riding around in that powerful metal machine makes him feel like Hercules, I suppose."

"Well, I'm impressed," Immy said, awed. "I'm thinking of driving my father's car to Weston on Sunday to pay a surprise visit to the folks, but I couldn't handle one of those monstrosities."

"I just hope James can," Helen said drily.

When Imogen arrived at the park the following afternoon, Morgan was already there. She saw him before he saw her, and deliberately made her face impassive as he jumped up with a ready smile from the bench where he was sitting. He made to shake her hand and she touched his briefly, then drew away as she sat down.

"I told you I couldn't stay long. What is it you have to say?" she enquired coolly.

"Immy, don't be like this," he said softly.

"Is that it? If this was all a ploy to get me here—" She half rose, and his face sobered at once.

"It's not. But I thought you should know what people are saying about you."

She stared at him, not understanding. All around them, people were laughing and enjoying themselves on a Saturday afternoon in the park. Small boys were sailing wooden boats on the lake, and pretending they were Drake or pirates. A man was flying a brightly coloured kite, his children cheering as its long tail snaked up into the sky. The rippling blue of the lake glittered like diamonds in the afternoon sun, and everything was perfectly normal, except for the chill that had suddenly filled Imogen's heart.

"Saying about me? What do you mean? Why on earth should anyone have anything to say about me?"

"You were seen, Immy. And gossiped about. I hope I've stopped it, but I thought you ought to know."

"Are you going to explain, Morgan, or am I supposed to guess what rubbish you're talking about?"

"I hope it's rubbish, cariad. I thought I knew you well enough to believe that."

"Tell me this minute, or I'm leaving," she snapped. She suspected that this was his way of getting around her again – and somehow, here in the daylight, now that she was used to the fact that he was still in the world, she was absolutely sure that she no longer wanted him. It was almost a shock, but a perfectly wonderful one.

"You visited the hotel where that chap Preston was staying," Morgan said flatly. "You were seen in the garden with him early one morning."

Imogen stared at him. He wasn't making sense. *Seen* with him early one morning? What was that meant to imply?

When she realised, her face flooded with colour, and she felt faint with a far more unpleasant kind of shock.

"You can't believe what you're saying," she whispered.

"I didn't say I believed it. I think I know you better than that, Immy. I'm just telling you what was overheard. If you should go there again, you'd better take great care."

"I won't be going there again. He's gone – and anyway, it wasn't at all like you're trying to imply. If you must know, we were having a furious row."

"I don't need to know the details. I'm just saying you should be careful in future. Dirt sticks."

She swallowed. He was making something sordid out of something that had been so innocent, so well meant on behalf of a friend…but if he was doing so, then so must those who had passed the rumour on.

"How did you hear about it?" she said huskily.

"A chambermaid who works there has a sister who cleans at the office. They were discussing it and one of the juniors heard them and came to me, thinking I'd like to hear a juicy bit of gossip. His words, not mine, but when I realised who he was talking about, I squashed it at once. I don't think you'll have any more trouble."

"Well, thank you for that."

He caught hold of her hand and squeezed it, and she let it lie there for a moment. His voice softened.

"Did you think I wouldn't defend you, Immy? You know I think too much of you for that. I always have."

She pulled her hand away from his and stood up. "Morgan we can never mend what's irretrievably broken. I'm grateful for what you did, but let's just leave it there."

"Do you really mean that?"

"Believe me, I mean it. Goodbye, Morgan."

She walked away with her head held high. She felt humiliated at the thought of being the subject of gossip, but she wouldn't let him see it. She was the cool and collected Miss Imogen Caldwell – and she had no intention of crawling away as if she had something to hide.

It was galling to think she couldn't go and tell Helen what the meeting with Morgan had been all about, but if she did that, Helen would know she had gone to confront Robert, and that the ensuing gossip was all her fault.

Immy knew she couldn't let that happen. Helen had been too traumatised by the whole thing to risk shattering her world all over again. As it was, she was putting the events in perspective with her usual resilience, but if the reason for Immy visiting the hotel ever came to light, she would be devastated.

Instead, Immy called her on the telephone as soon as she got home, rather than see her face to face. She told her crisply it was as they had thought. "MR's fling with that other girl is over and he wanted me to go back to him again. I told him what I thought of him, though."

"And that was all the mystery?" Helen said, clearly disappointed that there was to be no great drama unfolding.

"That was it. They don't always get their own way, Helen, and I relished telling him so."

"Nobody ever got their own way with you, darling," Helen said with a laugh. "Enjoy your day out tomorrow."

"I will," Immy said, but her hands were shaking slightly as she replaced the receiver, and she wasn't quite as confident as she sounded.

What if the gossip hadn't been stopped? What if it got to her father's ears? Or what if Morgan decided to do a little moral — or immoral — blackmailing on his own account in order to win her back? She wouldn't put that past him.

And who was becoming a cynic now? Immy asked herself crossly. She turned in relief as her brother Baz came breezing into the house on an unexpected Saturday afternoon visit home.

Chapter Twelve

An hour after she had left home late the next morning, having had a sandwich and cold drink to keep her going, Immy began to doubt that the solo driving trip was such a good idea after all.

Inside her cotton gloves, her hands were clammy. She knew she was gripping the steering-wheel far too tightly, but she couldn't seem to judge the distance between the car and the grass verge as well as when Robert had been guiding her.

Thinking of him set her teeth on edge. She was determined to do this all by herself. She had set herself a goal, and she didn't intend to be beaten. She prayed that other cars on the road would give her a wide berth, though the occasional horse and cart made her hold her breath in case the horse should rear up or take fright, sensing a novice driver. Didn't animals have an instinct about somebody nearby expiring with nerves, or was that all a myth…?

"For pity's sake, get hold of yourself, girl," she muttered to herself as she negotiated the winding lanes and narrow roads that seemed endlessly longer than they had the times her father had been driving.

At last the sign on the road told her she was nearing her destination. She could swear the smell of salt was in the air now, and with a wave of nostalgia she remembered when her parents used to take the older Caldwell children on regular visits to their aunt and uncle. Frances had always promised a penny to the first one to spot the sea.

How long ago and how dear it all seemed now. And how *sad*, knowing that such days could never come again. She drew a deep breath, knowing she was in danger of becoming maudlin, and it wouldn't do.

Aunt Rose would think there was something wrong with her, and Uncle Bertie would get all gruff and embarrassed. So she straightened her shoulders and got on with it, telling herself that the dampness in her eyes was simply due to a bit of dust from the road, and nothing more.

–

She finally stopped the car outside Aunt Rose's house with a huge sense of relief, choosing to forget for the moment that she had to drive it all the way back again. Instead, she allowed herself a surge of triumph, because she had actually done it. She was here, unscathed – and, once she had got her breath back, quite ready to brag about her achievement.

She stepped out of the car, her legs shaking only fractionally, and paused for a moment as she heard the sound of laughter coming from the garden.

Childish shrieks were coupled with the deeper, older laughter of adults, and just for a moment she let herself imagine it was themselves a dozen years ago, before Teddy was born…Immy and Elsie and Daisy and the infant Baz, playing their favourite games with their delightful mother and father in the garden at home.

Selfishly, Immy longed for those days to return with a fierceness that almost overwhelmed her, until the vision cleared, and she knew how foolish she was being.

She didn't know *what* was wrong with her today, she thought crossly, but, needing to blame someone, she put the blame squarely and unfairly on to Morgan Raine.

She pushed open the gate, hearing the familiar squeak of the hinges. Uncle Bertie always said cheerfully that he left it deliberately to warn them of strangers in the camp. Today there was so much noise it seemed that no one else noticed it.

Bertie was on his hands and knees on the grass, playing trains with three small boys and a yapping dog. Aunt Rose was sitting on a deck-chair knitting, after her usual gargantuan exertions with the Sunday dinner.

It was such a homely, cameo scene that Immy wanted to cherish it forever – until one of the little boys turned to stare at her in disbelief, and the mood was broken.

"It's our Immy," Teddy yelled, hurling himself at her, almost pulling her down. "Our Immy's come to see me!"

Rose stood up at once, her knitting falling to the ground as she moved swiftly towards her niece.

"My dear girl, what's wrong?" she said at once. "Where's your father?"

"Nothing's wrong! Why should there be? Oh, I know I should have called you to say I was coming, but I wanted to give you a surprise. I drove here by myself!"

"You *what*?" Bertie was beside her now, enveloping her in his usual bear hug. "You mean your father allowed you to drive his pride and joy? I didn't even know you knew how."

"Well, I do. Aren't you a little bit proud of me?"

"I've always been proud of you, my love. I'm afraid you've got here too late for Sunday dinner, though."

"Oh, we can always rustle up something," Aunt Rose said easily. "We'll leave you to your own devices while

Immy and I go into the kitchen, dear. Daisy's gone out with that friend of hers, Immy, but they'll both be back in time for tea."

Once inside the house she looked at Immy quizzically.

"Now then, my love, what's *really* wrong? I'm sure there's no illness in the family, or I'd have heard, so it must be something else. And I'd say it's something to do with the heart rather than the head. Am I right?"

"It's nothing, really."

"Whenever someone says 'it's nothing, really', you can be sure it's *something* really. So out with it before you burst and be sure it will go no further than these four walls."

"I shouldn't really say anything. It's not my secret to tell," Immy said at last.

"Then you'd better not tell me," Rose said firmly. "Unless you're involved, of course. Are you, Imogen?"

"Yes. I feel responsible, and I can't rid myself of the guilt, even though I know how ridiculous it is. I mean, how was I to know she would take such a fancy to him, and that he would turn out to be such a – such a—"

"A rat?" Rose supplied.

When Immy nodded, she went on thoughtfully.

"You know, darling, no one could ever take your mother's place, and it would be stupid and heartless to try. But if she were here, and if she saw you in such distress, I know she would want you to confide in her. Won't you let me try to be a substitute, just this once?"

It hadn't occurred to Immy until that moment how important this was to her aunt. Rose would have loved a daughter, and the Caldwell girls were the nearest she had ever got to having one of her own.

So she found herself pouring out all the trauma Helen had gone through with Robert Preston and telling her aunt how she had helped Helen through the night, and then gone storming off to Robert's hotel to have it out with him.

"You should have seen him, Aunt Rose," Immy said, finally allowing her mouth to stretch into a tremulous smile now that the worst of the telling was over. "Helen had really packed a punch, as they say in the pictures. He had a lovely bruise on his face. The next thing we heard was that he had been recalled to York, which made Elsie very happy, of course, because it meant that Joe came back to Bristol yesterday."

"And?" Rose said patiently.

"Well, that's it. It's a relief to get it off my chest – but it's our secret now, isn't it?"

"Of course, but why don't you tell me the rest of it?"

"Are you psychic or something? How do you know there's something else?"

"I know when one of my girls is troubled, and you haven't told me everything, have you? That's Helen's story, but what's yours, my love?"

Immy looked down at her hands for a moment. Then she unclasped them and gazed out of the window.

"I had a young man once," she said slowly.

If she thought her aunt would be shocked by all that she had to say, she was mistaken. In the telling, Immy was able to put Morgan Raine ever further into the past, and her aunt made it clear that she doubted that the gossips would make anything more of her little expedition to the hotel to confront Robert.

"They'll have forgotten it by now, because something more interesting will have occurred. It's the nature of the hotel business and the people who work there," Rose said sagely.

"But you don't really think I committed a *faux pas*, do you?" Immy said anxiously.

"Of course I don't, not for a minute. Now then, do you want something to eat, or not?"

Immy gave her a beatific smile, the first one in ages, it seemed to her. "I certainly do. I'm suddenly ravenous."

By the time Daisy and her pale friend Lucy came back from the farm, Immy had made friends with the evacuee children, and promised that when she came again she'd go to the beach with them all.

"We've had a wonderful time today," Daisy announced, when she had got over her astonishment at seeing Immy there.

Immy was equally astonished at seeing how grown up her sister seemed since the last time she had seen her. Daisy had grown apart from the rest of her family, she thought, but that was the way of things and there was no changing it.

"What have you been doing?" Rose asked indulgently.

"Riding, of course, and watching the airmen."

"*Daisy!*"

"Oh, it's all right, Aunt Rose. Part of Lucy's farm backs on to the airfield, and some of the recruits were doing their marching routines or whatever it is they call it. Ben knows a couple of the new ones, and he says they're going to start doing hurdling exercises on the promenade on Saturdays. They have to get fit for when they start flying practice. We're going to watch. Doesn't it sound like fun?"

"I'm not so sure about you watching these young men—"

"Oh, everyone will be there, not just us! We'll take the boys if you like."

Daisy caught Immy's glance and read it correctly. *Any excuse*, it said – but by now the boys were leaping about excitedly, and they all knew there would be no stopping them.

"So how's the work going, Daisy? Father said I was to ask you especially," Immy said, when she could make her voice heard above the din. "You haven't killed anybody yet, I hope?"

It was a testimony to the passing of time that they could say such things light-heartedly now, without feeling guilt on behalf of their mother, Immy thought. It wasn't that they had forgotten her, or ever could, but you couldn't wear sackcloth and ashes forever.

"I like it a lot," Daisy said, more soberly, adding cheekily, "I hope war won't come for a while yet, though, so that I'll be old enough to join up and be a proper nurse when it does."

"That's an awful thing to say! I hope it won't come at all," Immy said, thinking instantly of James Church and his tank, and the unpleasant possibility of young men she knew being wounded – or worse. She shied away from the thought.

"There's no chance of that hope, my love," Uncle Bertie told her. "It's a question of when, not if."

"But how can you be so sure?"

"How can you not, when all the signs are there? When all the newspapers and wireless reports are so full of gloom, and the government is giving us hints a mile high?"

He nodded towards the evacuees squabbling noisily with Teddy over who was going to be the engine driver now.

"And we wouldn't have these little inkspots with us if it wasn't for the threat of war, so at least we can be thankful for something, if not much else lately."

It was an odd way of looking at things, Immy thought as she took her leave of them all several hours later and started on the drive back to Bristol. It was an odd way for Rose and Bertie to finally have their house filled with children's laughter, the way they had always wanted it.

All because of a beloved sister-in-law's death, and the threat of a war. If this was God's will, He had a funny way of determining things for people.

She gave up philosophising, and concentrated on the road, realising that she was a deal more confident behind the wheel now than when she had started out.

It was partly because she had done it once and knew she could do it again. And everyone knew that the road home was never as long as the road that took you away from it.

But it was also partly because of the catharsis of unburdening herself to Aunt Rose and hearing her logical response to it all. Uncle Bertie always said that nothing was so bad that it couldn't be fixed, and for once, she believed it.

Her father greeted her with relief when she arrived home, commenting that he was glad his car was still in one piece, and so was she.

"I'm not sure which of those comes first in your mind," she said with a smile, "but I'll take it that you meant it kindly, Father."

"Of course I did."

"So where is everybody? Where's Elsie? I'm dying to tell her how well I did."

"She's out for a walk with Joe, so you'll just have to tell me how everybody is – unless you want to bore the Marys with your driving tales. They'd like to hear it, actually," he added. "I mentioned where you'd gone when I saw them going to church, and they think you're a very modern young lady."

"Do they?" Immy said with a grin. Not half as modern as she had once thought herself in certain areas. "Oh, I don't think I'll go up to them. I'm pretty tired tonight."

"Oh, well. But did you know Mary Yard was a munitions worker in the Great War? She was interested when I said one of the Bristol factories is stepping up production of aeroplane parts. Old ladies are never just old ladies, Immy. They would appreciate a chat with a bright young girl like you."

She sighed. "All right, then, if you think I should. I dare say I'm too wound up to sleep yet, anyway."

She hadn't had much to do with the Marys; why should she? They were just the upstairs tenants. Elsie had spent some time with them, though, and they weren't really old; they just seemed it. But half an hour wouldn't hurt...

A couple of hours later, after several cups of tea, she was still mesmerised by the tales the two of them had to tell. Their neat sitting-room was full of old-fashioned knick-knacks and potted plants, and she had looked through a dozen photograph albums. They were stuffed with sepia photos of young men in unfamiliar uniforms, newspaper cuttings about daring deeds and formal occasions, and more sombre ones too.

"This was my Harry," Mary Yard said in matter-of-fact tones, pointing to a handsome young man in a captain's uniform. "He was killed in the last push of the war, so we were never able to celebrate victory together. Mary's husband went even earlier."

"During Passchendaele." Mary Baxter nodded. Her sad eyes took on a faraway look. "Ever so handsome, he was. We'd only been married a month before he went. We wanted babies so badly, but we never got the chance to have them. We even named our boy. Raymond would have been twenty-three or four now."

"And just right for signing up for this next lot," Mary Yard, the more cynical of the pair, said.

"You think it's inevitable, then?" Immy said quickly.

"No doubt, my dear. Let's just hope there aren't as many widows left this time as there were in our day. Nor so many young lives wasted. Where are all those beautiful young men now? Just white crosses in a graveyard – and those are the lucky ones, leaving something behind to grieve over."

The other Mary chipped in. "Oh yes. There were thousands who didn't get any grave at all. Just blown away to dust as if they were nothing. It makes you wonder what it's all about, doesn't it? Is that what you're born for? To grow up and fall in love and then get cut down in your prime? Sometimes it's hard to equate all that with a loving God."

"But you still go to church every Sunday," Immy reminded her, guiltily knowing that she only went on occasion.

"Of course," Mary Yard said in surprise, as if there could be any doubt. "If you don't believe in something, what have you got left?"

"Anyway, dear," Mary Baxter went on, "my advice is that if you've got a young man and you love him, then you should marry him and make the most of him. I told your sister the same thing. Enjoy every day, because it will never come again."

"My goodness, all this is getting too solemn for me," Immy said. She spoke gently, however; she could see that these two sweet-faced ladies meant every word they said, and no doubt Elsie would have taken them very seriously.

Mary Yard laughed. "Oh, you young things only think about your careers these days. But we did it right, didn't we, Mary? We were both quite a bit older than you when we married, and we cherish every day we had with our sweethearts."

And now all they have are memories, Immy thought as she went back to her own room. Neither of the ladies had remarried, though presumably they could have done.

As she undressed for bed, Immy couldn't get the conversation out of her mind. It had really touched her soul, she realised. In an unlikely fashion, it was if she had suddenly received a deep understanding of something very fundamental. She had recognised that what those two faded ladies had known was real love. *Real* love, not shabby fumbling on a hillside or in a motor car. Not the kind you saw portrayed at the pictures, all glossy and fake. Real love. The kind that neither she nor Helen yet knew. The kind of love Elsie had with Joe.

–

Daisy Caldwell knew she had found her vocation at last. In the hospital some of the patients and proper nurses had begun calling her "Daisy-Daisy" after the silly song.

She didn't mind. She was the youngest auxiliary on the wards, and the patients said it made them feel better just looking at her, because she was bright and cheerful and pretty. She hadn't been asked to do anything *too* nasty yet, she admitted, but if she had to, she was sure she could cope. She wanted to be a nurse, and a good one.

She was trying really hard to persuade Lucy to join her. So far, she had resisted, but Daisy knew she had a stronger personality than her friend and hoped to bring her round to the idea in time.

"You shouldn't try to coerce her, my love," Aunt Rose told her. "It takes a certain kind of person to be a nurse, and if Lucy doesn't have the stomach for it, it would be wrong to force her into it."

"I bet nobody said that in the Great War when you were all keen to do your bit, Aunt Rose," Daisy said slyly. "Didn't you help with the ambulance service?"

"Yes, but you and I are the same kind of people, Daisy. Strong-willed and willing to get on with things, no matter what we're asked to do. Whereas I'm not so sure about Lucy. She doesn't have a lot of stamina, and I've noticed she has that worrying cough all the time."

"She tends the horses when they're not well, and you have to be a bit tough on a farm. She's not as soft as she looks," Daisy defended her. She was more pleased at being compared with her forthright aunt than she let on, however.

"Oh, well," Rose said, laughing. "Perhaps she should be a vet instead of a doctor, then."

Daisy shuddered. "I've seen the vet at the farm, and I know I couldn't do some of the things he has to do."

"Then we won't think about them, and we certainly won't talk about them," Rose said briskly, remembering the unpleasantness of George's recent worming problem.

"Agreed," Daisy said, perking up. "I'll see you later then, Aunt Rose. I promised to meet Lucy at the beach."

"Are you taking any of the boys with you?" Rose called out, but her niece had already gone, flying out of the house like the wind, her hair glowing in the sunlight, an absolute picture of health and glorious young womanhood, Rose thought fondly. And since such sentiments didn't often come to her practical mind, she yelled at the boys to stop making that racket this minute, or she'd box all their heads together.

But she was smiling as she said it, and she knew they didn't really believe her. Bertie had told them more than once that her bark was worse than her bite, and that she loved them all in her peculiar way. And so she did.

Whether the house rang with the sound of children's laughter, or squabbling, tears or tantrums, she was fulfilled in a way she never had been before. She was more than content, and she refused to look ahead to a time when it would all have to change. As they all knew it must.

–

Daisy caught sight of Lucy sitting forlornly on the sea wall overlooking the wide sweep of sand that made up Weston Bay. The sea was its usual distant glimmer on the horizon, with the hazy view of Wales across the Channel, and unless you were fated to catch sight of the tide or studied the posted details of the times it appeared, you sometimes marvelled that it ever came in twice a day to wash the sand clean at all. The fact that boats were beached haphazardly and mournfully on the mud at the Knightstone end of the bay were the only reminders that any craft ever rode majestically on a full tide.

"Why are you looking so glum?" Daisy demanded, the minute she joined her friend. "You look really pasty today,

Lucy. Honestly, you could brighten yourself up a bit. You look as if you've lost a sixpence and found a penny."

"You'd be miserable if you felt like I did."

"How *do* you feel, then? You're not ill, are you? Shall I practise my nursing skills and save you?"

She was laughing, teasing her friend as she so often did, but to her horror she saw Lucy's eyes well up.

"My mother made me go to the doctor about my cough, and I have to see a special man for a second opinion."

"A second opinion about what?"

Her heart beat faster as she saw Lucy's lips tremble. With her new-found knowledge – even though it amounted to little more than snippets gleaned from the nurses at the hospital and from Aunt Rose's medical books – Daisy knew darned well that a second opinion meant something serious was suspected.

"You'd better not touch me or come too close," Lucy said abruptly. "Not until we know for sure. They say it's catching. I'm not sure if horses can catch it, though."

"Lucy, for goodness' sake, tell me what's wrong! You're scaring me now."

"It might be TB. Consumption. Whatever they call it. Don't know yet."

Her voice was jerky with fear. And to her shame, Daisy felt herself edge slightly away from her. But she knew enough to know that Lucy was right. TB – consumption – whatever name you put on it – was highly infectious. It took forever to cure, and the only treatment was rest and sunlight and cold air and taking life easy in a sanatorium for months at least.

There would be no nursing career, no horse riding, nothing but rest and boredom for a sixteen-year-old.

"Lucy, I don't know what to say. I'm knocked side-ways."

"What is there to say? Anyway, we don't know for sure yet. Might be nothing. But let's keep well apart for now, right?"

Her eyes were steadier now, huge in her pale face, daring Daisy to mock her this time, to pooh-pooh the thought that anything could be really wrong with her. Wanting Daisy to give her the dignity she deserved.

"Right," Daisy said. "Just until we know for sure."

"Ben brought me here in the truck today," she went on. "I didn't feel up to riding my bike. He had to see somebody in town, and he'll be collecting me in a while. I'm sorry, Daisy. I didn't want to come out at all really, but I couldn't tell you on the phone, either. It wouldn't have seemed right."

"No. It wouldn't."

All of a sudden there seemed to be a great distance yawning between them. Not so much physically, despite the self-imposed few feet between them, but the distance that illness made. It separated people.

Daisy knew that from her own mother. She knew it from the hospital visitors who came to see their nearest and dearest and couldn't think of anything to say except the most trivial and trite words. Illness prevented people opening their hearts, at a time when they most needed to.

There was a small, embarrassed silence, and they both turned with relief as Ben tooted at them. Lucy stood up and brushed down her skirt.

"I'd better go. I'll ring you as soon as I hear any news. Or you can ring me. You can't catch anything over the phone – at least, I don't think so," she added, scared and uncertain of what might be happening to her, and the effect it would have on every single thing in her life from now on.

"Of course I'll phone you," Daisy said roughly. "And I'll find out everything I can about you-know-what, just in case. But I'm sure it'll turn out to be nothing, and we'll be laughing about it very soon."

And without a second thought, she pulled Lucy to her and hugged her close. No damned disease was going to make her turn her back on her best friend, she thought fiercely.

She sat on the sea wall for a long while after Ben and Lucy had gone, still shocked by what she had heard. She was in no state to go back to Aunt Rose's yet. She just sat, breathing in the salty air, absorbing the carefree sounds of high summer like a sponge, and registering none of it. Not the visitors, nor the donkey rides, the beach games, the ice-cream vendors, the swooping, screaming gulls or the flurries of sand that blurred the eyes. And it wasn't only the sand that stung so painfully.

Eventually, she began to walk aimlessly along the beach, needing to clear her head and try to make sense of it all. Lucy had always seemed so active, if a little on the puny side compared to her robust family with their traditional farmers' rosy cheeks. That delicacy of skin had been something to envy, though, not to think of as ominous.

"Somebody seems to be lost in dreamland," she heard a voice say teasingly. She realised she had been walking with her head down and had almost barged into someone.

Someone large and lean, with laughing brown eyes and a wide smile. Someone wearing a checked, open-necked shirt and casual trousers who stood squarely in front of her now.

"Excuse me. I'm sorry," she mumbled, but as she went to move sideways, so did he. He blocked her path, and she glared at him irritably. She wasn't in the mood to exchange pleasantries, even with a young man who would certainly have caught her attention at any other time.

"Where's the fire?" he asked.

"*Excuse* me?" she said again, more haughtily this time.

"Haven't I seen you somewhere before?"

Daisy sighed. She had been to the pictures often enough to know that this was a line that actors employed. She didn't think this one was an actor, of course – he didn't have that starry, unreachable look. He just had a nice face.

"I doubt it. Will you let me pass, please?"

"I know where it was. You and that other girl have been watching us through the perimeter fence a couple of times. It's a devil when you can't remember something, isn't it? I'm Callum, by the way. Cal to my friends."

Daisy automatically took the hand he was holding out to her. As she did so, she got the most extraordinary feeling. She would have liked to report to Lucy that it was love at first sight, and that a tingling sensation ran right through her entire body, the way the love stories told you it would.

What she actually felt was a sense of horror that she was touching this young man with the hand that had recently touched Lucy's. If she had caught something from her friend, she was probably passing it on to him.

She shook off the feeling blindly, but she couldn't stop trembling, and her knees threatened to buckle beneath her.

"Here, are you all right? You look as if you're going to pass out. I don't usually have such an effect on people," she

215

heard Callum – Cal – say in concern. "Sit down on the sand for a minute. I can call someone if you like. There's always ambulance people around somewhere."

"I don't need anybody. I'm all right," Daisy muttered, but she did as she was told and sat down abruptly on the warm sand. He sat beside her, rubbing her hands between his, as if she was chilled and needed her blood warmed.

"What are you, a bloody doctor or something?" she snapped, immediately appalled at saying such a thing. "Letting yourself down," she could almost hear Aunt Rose say.

Cal smiled. "Hardly. Just an RAF erk."

"A what?"

"The lowest of the low, in RAF parlance. Just starting my training at Locking Camp."

It all became clear now. He probably hadn't been stringing her a line at all. He must have seen her and Lucy looking over the fence and watching the RAF boys going through their paces. It was easier for them to place two girls than for the girls to recognise any of the large group of young men.

"I'm sorry I was so rude just now," she said humbly. "I'd just heard a bit of worrying news, and I was trying to get used to it."

"That's all right. About you being rude, I mean. Not about the worrying news. Bad luck. Want to tell me about it? It sometimes helps."

"Certainly not. It's private."

What was she doing here, sitting on the sands with a young man when they hadn't been properly introduced, and he didn't even know her name? She groaned inside at the primness of her own thoughts, but her head was still in a total muddle. Some nurse she would be, if Lucy's news threw her into such panic…but nurses dealt mostly with strangers, not best friends, and that made a difference.

"How about an ice-cream, then? Or a donkey ride? Or we could always paddle in the mud. Weston's famous for it, I understand."

God, he was persistent! She started to smile, despite herself, and he looked relieved.

"That's better. What's your name, by the way?"

"Daisy," she said, without thinking, before she could start to wonder why the dickens she should tell him.

"So, Daisy, give me your answer, do," he said. "I think an ice-cream's favourite, isn't it?"

"Don't you ever take no for an answer?"

"No," he said, and they both started to laugh as if he had said something excruciatingly funny.

"All right. Just an ice cream, then."

After all, she thought, watching him go off to one of the vendors, sitting on the sands eating an ice-cream with a nice young man would make no difference at all to the outcome of things. Not to Lucy's problem, or the prospect of a war, or whether she would make a good nurse.

It didn't mean she didn't concern herself with any of those things, but just for now, while she could, she was putting it all to the back of her mind.

Chapter Thirteen

Daisy wasn't going to tell anybody about Cal. Normally she would have confided in Lucy, but she didn't think that was wise until they knew what was happening. She certainly couldn't tell Aunt Rose, who would be scandalised to think she had virtually allowed herself to be "picked up", as they said.

Then again, she might not, Daisy mused, since Aunt Rose was more progressive in her thinking than many women her age. But she couldn't take the risk. Not when something as delicately fragile as a blossoming relationship with a young man was concerned. If it *was* a relationship.

She shivered at the very thought of the word. It sounded almost too decadent. And it wasn't really blossoming, either, she thought with brutal honesty. It was more like – well, more like *budding*. He'd only bought her an ice-cream, and he hadn't said anything about seeing her again. Only in the most casual way.

"We're going to be doing exercises on the promenade at the weekends," he'd said. "Hurdling and so on."

"I know. My friend told me."

"Maybe you'll be watching that too, then," he'd said with a grin. "I'll try not to make a fool of myself, tripping over my big feet."

"And I'll try not to laugh if I see you doing it."

And that had been that. It was hardly big-time passion, Daisy thought gloomily, her head stuffed full of Hollywood romances. He probably thought she was too young for it, anyway. He had joined up, so he was obviously older than her, probably eighteen or nineteen or more. He'd think she was still a child.

It was one more depressing thing to think about at the end of a depressing day, by which time she had studied her aunt's medical books to find out all she could about the disease that used to be called consumption and was now known as TB. She supposed it was a mite less intimidating than its proper name of tuberculosis, but people still died of it.

She couldn't bear to think of Lucy dying. You never thought of young people dying. Dying was for older people, not for girls. Nor for boys who dressed up in uniforms and thought themselves men and went off to war – and that hadn't really occurred to her before, either.

Did she *really* want to be a nurse? The answer came with surprising ferocity. Yes, she damned well did. She might never be a Marie Curie or a Doctor-Foster-went-to-Gloucester, thank you very much, she thought childishly, but she wanted to care for people.

Her mother had enchanted and uplifted her audiences with her dancing, and it had taken time for Daisy to realise that she didn't want to do the same thing, and why.

There could only ever be one Frances Caldwell, and in Daisy's eyes no one could ever follow her. And whether or not it was egotistical, Daisy knew she couldn't bear to be a second-rate anything. Instead she would be a first-rate nurse. It was decided.

"They're really getting serious about evacuating folk out of the cities now, especially London," Bertie remarked a few weeks later, his head deep in his morning paper as usual. "From the sound of it, they'll be practically empty soon, and the countryside's population will have swelled by millions."

"It's just as well we got our little charmers while the going was good then, isn't it?" Rose said smartly. "We did well for ourselves, didn't we?"

She beamed fondly at Ronnie and Norman, busy scooping up their breakfast cereal as fast as they could in competition with Teddy. She knew she should scold them, but it did no harm, and there were worse things in life to contend with. Having heard the shocking news about poor little Lucy Luckwell being sent off to some sanatorium, a bit of leeway at breakfast seemed nothing to get het up about. Rose was just thankful that Daisy was taking it fairly well, even offering to exercise Lucy's horse for her, and writing to Lucy every week, since she wasn't allowed visitors outside the family for a while.

Daisy had made a point of finding out a lot more about Lucy's illness. She knew about the regular temperature and sputum checks, the vast quantities of milk and eggs Lucy had to swallow, and the need for rest. She responded by sending her books and magazines to read and writing her lots of letters.

Daisy was really showing what she was made of, Rose thought approvingly. Her mother would have been proud.

–

"*I saw Cal again on Saturday afternoon,*" Daisy wrote in one of her letters to Lucy, unable to keep it to herself any longer.

It's a shame you didn't meet him. Though perhaps I shouldn't be too sorry about that! He might have fancied you more than me. Not that I know if he fancies me or not.

I wonder how you can tell. He waves to me if I see him over your fence when I'm taking Star out for exercise, but he can't make it so obvious when he's hurdling on the promenade. Too many people around. But that's the trouble. I never see him alone. But do I want to?

It's a bit scary in a way, and I don't really know what I feel about him. My heart beats faster as soon as I see him, in a kind of sick way. I know that sounds odd, but I can't think of any other way to say it. I probably couldn't say it out loud at all, but it's much easier writing it all down and knowing you wouldn't tell anybody.

I do miss you, Lucy, but at least I can write masses and masses to you and know that my secret's safe with you. That's a laugh, too, isn't it? It's not exactly much of a secret. Not exactly the grand passion, as they say. Oh well.

She ended with lots of kisses, knowing guiltily that until Lucy was better, they were safer on paper than on lips.

She didn't say how frustrating it all was, either, because that was a word that was somehow a little suspect, a little *risqué*. But it was how she felt. Frustrated. Even thinking it made her feel a little peculiar, the way it felt when you wanted something you couldn't have. Except she wasn't quite sure what it was she wanted.

Elsie Caldwell knew exactly what it was she wanted. There was nothing so heavenly as basking in the knowledge that you were in love, and that your beloved was every bit as much in love with you. It was the most magical feeling on earth, and made you feel expansive towards the whole world, wanting everyone to share in the euphoria it brought.

She didn't think her sister Imogen had felt it yet, and Daisy was too young. Immy's friend Helen was too bright and breezy and cynical to fall for a man, but she – Elsie Caldwell – was so in love she sometimes thought she would die from it. Except that of course she wouldn't.

Not unless Joe died with her and they could continue loving one another far above the clouds on some blissful, ethereal plane...

"I wish I could see inside your mind and see just what it is you're thinking about," Joe said lazily, as they lay on the grass in the park that Sunday afternoon. "Your eyes are half closed, and your mouth has gone all dreamy and relaxed in a half smile. It's also extremely kissable. If we weren't in a public place, I would do something about it right now."

Elsie opened her eyes at once, twisting her head to gaze up at him. The smile widened.

"I was just thinking how lucky we are. So many things had to happen to bring you here, Joe, to bring you into my life. When I think about how happiness depends on such a thread, and how different it might have been, it makes me shudder."

His hand closed over hers, warm and strong.

"Well, don't even think about it. Nor about the past. The future's what matters, yours and mine, and the fact that we'll always be together from now on."

"Will we?" she said, her heart giving a leap of pure joy. "You're sure of that, are you?"

"As sure as any of us can be, sweetheart."

He didn't want to spoil this lovely day by any talk of war, even though the moment it came – or possibly sooner – he would do the same as every other patriotic man did for his country. Only cowards or conscientious objectors would remain behind while the rest of them enlisted.

Elsie wasn't stupid, however, and as she sat up to look down at him, a grey cloud hovered over the edge of the sun, gilding it with a rare golden beauty only an artist could capture. For a moment the air went a shade cooler, and she shivered.

"I know what it is you're not saying, Joe, and I thank you for it. But we all read the newspapers and listen to the wireless – we can't help it at home, as my father has it on night and day – and we have to be realistic, don't we?"

"I'm afraid we do, darling," he said gently, his fingers lightly caressing her bare arm with feather-light strokes that curled her toes and thrilled her senses.

If he knew…if he only knew, thought Elsie achingly, how she longed for him to make love to her. Wicked though it was for a well-brought-up girl to think that way, – and dangerous too, in view of the possible consequences – she ached for him so much. She dreamed of it too, with no idea if those dreams were anything like reality.

She had never told him, or anyone. Once she had thought of telling Immy, when she fancied there might have been a spark of something between her and that Welsh fellow. But Immy had got all closed up lately and spent all her spare time with Helen Church – or in talking to the Marys, surprisingly enough – rather than staying at home. And anyway, Elsie didn't want to share her dreams with anyone but Joe.

"If you have to join up" – she said it deliberately, facing the fear – "what will you do?"

"Army. Infantry, same as my father."

The fact that he said it so quickly, and so definitely, with unmistakable pride, told her far more than his actual words. She would never lose him to another woman, but she was going to lose him all the same, and to something far more lethal.

He sensed her mood at once, and pulled her down beside him, uncaring that other people might be glancing their way. Let them, Joe thought savagely. If all the world was supposed to love a lover, let them see true love.

"I want to ask you something, Elsie. War is coming – we both know that it must," he said. "I want to know before I have to leave you that you belong to me."

Elsie's heart throbbed wildly. She had so wanted to hear those words, wanted him to make love to her so badly…but when the moment came, could she do this? Could she really forsake all the principles she had ever learned, and could he really expect it of her?

Her mouth was dry as she tried to speak. She loved him so much, but she wasn't sure how she was going to answer him.

Joe's fingers stilled her lips.

"I'm not asking for an immediate answer, but I want you to marry me, Elsie," he said softly. "If I have to go away to war, I want to go knowing that we belong as man and wife."

"Oh, Joe," she croaked, ashamed of her doubts.

"We may not have known one another long, and I don't know what your father will think of this haste, but there could never be anyone else for me. If you feel the same, then I think we should get engaged right away."

He took his fingers away from her lips, and she stopped caring if the world was watching. She caught him to her and pressed her cheek to his.

"Of course I'll marry you, Joe," she breathed. "I want nothing more than to be your wife."

He kissed her then, in full view of a small family taking a boat-ride on the lake. And nobody minded. It was summer, the dark shadow had already bypassed the sun, and war clouds hadn't yet filled the sky.

"I'll ask your father formally tonight," he promised. "And then I shall buy you the biggest diamond I can find."

"Or three smaller ones," she said. "I always liked the idea of three diamonds. It sounds silly, but it always makes me think of a family. Mother, father and baby. Or am I being too forward?" she said, going pink.

"You're delightful," Joe said, loving her.

–

They were totally taken aback by Quentin's reaction. Elsie had been so sure of her father's liking for Joe that she had begged to be allowed to come with him when he made the formal request for her hand.

How *very* formal that sounded, she thought, when he was asking for so much more than her hand. For all of her, body and soul, for the rest of their lives…

"Have you forgotten so soon, girl?" Quentin said angrily, looking past Joe to his daughter.

"Forgotten what?" she stammered, as red-faced as if she had been caught out in some childhood misdemeanour.

But she wasn't a child. She was a woman, and a man loved her and wanted to marry her. Her father had no right to diminish her like this. Enraged, she rushed on before Joe could say any more.

"You must have expected this, Daddy, and I don't understand you. I thought you'd be pleased. I thought you'd want me to be happy."

In the next instant she saw the anguish in his eyes, and she knew. She thought about how often he went quiet in the middle of an ordinary evening, going to his room and closing the door, from behind which would emanate the faint sounds of his gramophone playing one of Frances's favourite songs.

It was his way of keeping her alive and keeping her close to him. She knew how difficult it was for him to express his grief, and how deeply that grief went.

Joe stood in silent embarrassment as she ran to her father and put her arms around him, whispering close to his cheek.

"Oh, Daddy, I'm sorry. It's because of Mother, isn't it?"

He almost shook her off, his voice harsh with pain.

"She's not been gone nine months yet, and you expect me to think of wedding celebrations already? Have you *no* respect for her memory? Besides, you're far too young. You don't know what you want out of life yet."

"Yes, I do, Daddy. I want Joe. I'm lucky enough to have found a good man who loves me, and we want to be married. You and Mother set us a wonderful example, and we want to find the happiness that you had. Is that so terrible?"

This lovely day was turning out to be terrible, she thought. Somehow it was all going wrong, and she couldn't think what else to say — until Joe took up the cause.

"Mr Caldwell – Quentin – correct me if I'm speaking out of turn, but Elsie once said her aunt told her that you and your wife were married when she was about Elsie's age."

Quentin glowered angrily, but Joe went on relentlessly.

"It was wartime, and you desperately wanted to be together, and to feel that you belonged together. I believe Elsie's Aunt Rose said that the two of you thought it made you invincible, despite all the horror that war brings. Knowing you belonged in the eyes of God and the law was a kind of talisman for you. It's exactly the same for Elsie and me."

Elsie held her breath, wondering if he had stepped too far over the line. Her father wouldn't like to be reminded of what some might consider to be sentimental weakness, nor that Aunt Rose had been talking out of turn and revealing heartbreakingly private and personal truths.

She found herself clinging to Joe's hand, her eyes pleading with her father to understand, to remember what it had been like for him and her mother.

His tormented look finally slackened, and he spoke in more measured tones.

"I suppose I'm being selfish, very blind, and very foolish. As for a future son-in-law, I couldn't wish for a better man for my daughter than you, Joe. In normal circumstances I would insist that you have a long engagement to get to know one another properly. But these are not normal times, any more than they were in 1914."

As he paused, his voice faltering, Joe spoke firmly.

"Then does this mean we have your blessing, sir? I love Elsie with all my heart, and I'll never let her down."

"If I thought that, I'd do the Germans' work for you," Quentin said with grim humour.

"*So*, Daddy?" Elsie said, unable to bear any more of this hedging. *Men*...why didn't they just get on with it? It only needed one word...

"Patience, girl," her father answered with a small smile, then held out his hand to Joe. "Yes. You have my blessing."

Elsie gave a cry of pure delight and threw herself into his arms, and the three of them stood close together for a moment, arms entwined, one unit.

—

"It was awful for a while. I thought Daddy was going to have a blue fit!" Elsie told Immy excitedly, a long while later. She couldn't sleep and didn't intend to let anyone who would listen sleep either.

She sat on the foot of her sister's bed in her cotton nightgown, hugging her knees tight. With her excitedly glowing face scrubbed clean for bedtime, she looked about ten years old, Immy thought.

"I really thought Daddy was going to refuse. My heart was in my boots, until Joe reminded him of what Aunt Rose told us. He and Mother did marry young, and it *was* because of the war, so he didn't have a leg to stand on after that."

She sobered for a minute. "I did feel anxious for him, though, Immy. He looked quite stricken. But it couldn't have been that much of a shock for him, could it? He must have known how Joe and I feel about one another."

"Perhaps he realised he's about to lose you too, Elsie."

"What do you mean? I'm not going anywhere!"

"When you and Joe are married, you'll want a home of your own, won't you?"

"Well, of course, eventually. But I'm resigned to the fact that he'll be joining the army. He'll be away for most of the time until things get settled between Chamberlain and Hitler. So I shall carry on living here, and when Joe comes home on leave, we'll just share my room."

Her face flooded with colour at the thought, and her heart raced.

"That's what I mean, darling," Immy said softly. "Once you're married, you won't be Daddy's little girl any longer. He'll be losing you, even though you'll still be living here. Because you'll be living with Joe."

"It's a bit scary, isn't it? All *that*, I mean. You know, the intimate things. Even undressing…oh, I do love him madly, Immy, but I have no idea what to do, and Mother's not here to tell me."

"You could always ask Aunt Rose. She'd probably draw diagrams for you," Imogen said, starting to grin.

"I certainly could not!" Elsie hesitated. "You don't know any more than I do about it, I suppose?"

"Afraid not. Well, not *afraid*. But in answer to your unspoken question, no, I haven't experienced any of *that*."

After an awkward little pause, Elsie said: "I know what I'll do. I'll ask the Marys. They're both so nice, and I know they won't think I'm odd or forward or wicked or anything. I just want to get it *right*, you see. When the time comes, I don't want Joe to be sorry he married me."

Immy scrambled down the bed and gave her a hug.

"I think Joe will be very glad he married you, darling. He's a very lucky man."

Elsie shook her head, her eyes full of dreams.

"You're wrong, Immy. I'm the lucky one. I'm the luckiest girl on earth. And I'm going to bed now, or he'll be telling me off for being late at the shop tomorrow morning."

She laughed delightedly, blowing her sister a kiss as she left Immy's bedroom, knowing that even if she was late, it would simply be an excuse to go to Joe's office for a secret kiss before she started work for the day. She was sure of herself, and of him, and the future they were going to share, with the special kind of confidence that comes from being in love.

Immy envied that feeling. She thought she had known it once, but it had faded so quickly, she decided it hadn't really been love at all. At least, not the kind of love that would last a lifetime. It had been infatuation, and the thrill of being desired.

She moved restlessly in her bed, wishing she could find someone to love. No matter what happened in the months to come, Elsie would always have Joe coming home to her.

Unless the unthinkable happened, of course. A chill ran through her then, because people died in wartime. The Marys had both been as madly in love with their husbands as Elsie was with Joe, and they had both ended up as young widows.

Was it worth all the suffering afterwards? She asked herself the question seriously and knew that it was. The Marys had told her that. They wouldn't have missed a moment with their husbands – and anyway, you couldn't foretell the future. You had to grasp happiness where it came, and good luck to Elsie and Joe. It was funny, though. She had always been so sure she would be the first to marry…

–

"So when's the big day to be?" Aunt Rose said over the telephone when Elsie had bubbled out the news the following evening. "I shall need a new hat, of course. You must design one for me, Elsie – if you've got the time, that is."

"I'll have plenty of time. We don't intend to rush into it immediately, Aunt Rose. We're going to buy an engagement ring next weekend, though, and Joe's taking me up to Yorkshire to meet his family. I know his uncle and cousin, of course, but I have to meet his parents. I've already spoken to them on the phone when Joe told them the news, and they sounded really nice – when I could understand them!"

"Are they foreign or something?"

"No, of course not, but they do talk differently. Joe went to college and is educated, but they're country folk. Oh Lord, I hope that doesn't sound patronising. I don't mean it to!"

"I'm sure you don't, and I'm sure they'll love you, Elsie. So when's the big day?" she asked again.

"We haven't decided yet. Fairly soon, I think, but we haven't set the date yet."

"Elsie dear, if you need some advice of an intimate nature, you know you can come to me, don't you?" Rose offered delicately. "I think you know what I mean."

"It's all right, Aunt Rose, really. I have a book," Elsie explained, glad her aunt couldn't see her fiery cheeks. She hadn't intended the conversation to take this turn.

"Oh well, if you have a *book*, I suppose that's all right. I didn't know they printed such details nowadays, except in medical books, and I'm not sure I approve of it."

"Mrs Yard – Mary from upstairs – gave it to me earlier and explained a few things. It's all very proper. She was a nurse during the last war and thought it might be useful."

"I see. Well, that's all right then."

Before her aunt became too ruffled at being usurped in her duty by one of the Marys, Elsie quickly changed the direction of the conversation.

It had been far less embarrassing talking to the Marys. They had been so frank, assuring her that the act of making love for the first time was not something to be afraid of. Nor should the details be kept secret and furtive, in their opinion. They were something every bride had a right to know.

"And it really won't hurt too much?" Elsie had asked apprehensively.

"If you love and trust one another, and your young man is gentle and takes his time, it will be no more than a momentary sting, my dear, and maybe not even that," Mary Yard had told her.

And yes, there *were* diagrams in the book the Marys had given her. It still seemed an awesome thing to happen, this transformation in a man's body that was the means of making love...of making babies. Elsie, who had never touched her own private parts, except when she was bathing, wondered how she would ever get over the embarrassment at having someone else touching her there...seeing her...

"It's the most natural thing in the world," Mary Baxter had said gently, seeing her eyes darken with fright. "If it wasn't for the act of love, none of us would be here, my dear. *You* wouldn't be here. Without the act of love between a man and a woman the world would have ended before it even began. You read your Bible, don't you?"

"Oh yes," said Elsie hastily, knowing she hadn't read it properly in quite a while. "And Mother always used to read the stories to us when we were small."

She had choked a little then, remembering Frances's sweet, melodious voice relating the stories of Adam and Eve, and Moses, and of Jesus dying for them all. Magical stories that were fact and fable all rolled into one.

The other Mary added her own common-sense finale.

"As long as there's love and trust between you both, it will be as wonderful as you want it to be."

"I know we have that. And you don't think I'm too forward for asking you both such things?" she said anxiously.

"You're a very sensible girl," they assured her.

Chapter Fourteen

Sunday was the day that Baz made his duty visit home, and on the same day Joe arrived for a leisurely afternoon in the garden with his new fiancée, her sister and father. It was a gorgeously warm day, and even the Marys from upstairs had descended into the garden at Quentin's invitation.

Cook had made a fresh batch of lemonade and biscuits for the weekend, and Immy was in the act of fetching them from the kitchen — and wondering, idly and impossibly, if her father was taking more than a friendly interest in Mary Yard — when the front door bell rang.

She ran to answer it, throwing open the door, prepared to berate Baz for not coming to the back entrance as he always did.

"Have you lost your sense of direction since leaving home, you goose?" she said gaily, the words out of her mouth before she realised it wasn't her brother standing there at all, but two strangers.

At least, the dumpy little woman with the straggly grey hair and troubled eyes was a stranger. The other was a man she had seen before. He was weather-beaten, and obviously felt awkward at dressing up for Sunday. His collar was almost choking him, and his hands were gnarled with half the knuckles split. The ferryman.

"It's Mr Bray, isn't it?" Immy said quickly, a sense of foreboding almost knocking her sideways. "Enoch Bray."

"That's right, Miss," he said, almost humbly. "And this is my old lady, Sarah Bray."

The woman nodded, as if too afraid to smile. The small, cramped house at the waterfront where Baz lived with these two was really little more than a hovel, so presumably the tall house in Vicarage Street was somewhat intimidating.

It was all relative, of course, but the thoughts kept spinning around Immy's brain as if they were in a whirlpool. And everybody knew how a whirlpool could suck you down…

"What's happened? It's Baz, isn't it? Is he ill?"

Or worse…

"Oh, no, miss, he's not ill," Sarah Bray said at once, her old head nodding and bobbing as if to deny the words she said. How odd, thought Immy. It should be shaking fit to burst, to reassure her, and it was doing the exact opposite.

She gathered her stupid senses together, wondering why on earth she was analysing their behaviour at such a time. But she didn't have to wonder. She knew exactly why. It was to put off the moment…

"I'm forgetting my manners. Please come inside and tell me why you're here," she said. "It's far too hot to be standing on the doorstep."

Especially in those stuffy clothes. Indeed, there were beads of perspiration as big as mothballs on their foreheads. Immy was thankful they hadn't wanted to shake her hand, feeling the clamminess on her palms as if they had actually done so.

"Come on, Sarah," Enoch urged, as the woman hung back. "Miss Caldwell won't eat you, and it has to be done."

For pity's sake! Immy almost screamed as she ushered the two of them inside.

"Now, tell me what it is you've come to say," she ordered, as she closed the front door.

Her heart thudded uncomfortably. She didn't even offer them a seat. First things first. *Important* things first.

From the back garden she could hear the faint sounds of chatter and laughter, and her heart as well as her head told her it was a scene that was about to be shattered.

"He left this letter for us, and another one that we was to bring to your father, miss. We didn't know nothing until we got up this morning and found he'd gone. It was a terrible shock, and Sarah's still not over it. She were very fond of the boy, see, and allus treated him like her own."

The indignation in his voice was too much for Immy. Baz *wasn't* their own. He belonged to the Caldwells, and she couldn't forget that she had been the one to urge her father to let him go. It had been the price for Baz's silence over her half-baked love affair with Morgan.

She snatched the letter out of Enoch Bray's hand. His letter. She needed to see that first. Her father had to be the one to open his.

She recognised Baz's scrawling handwriting and careless spelling. He'd never been much of a scholar…as if any of that mattered now! She was furious at her own pathetic attention to detail.

"*Dear Enoch and Sarah,*" Baz had written.

> "*By the time you get this, I'll be gone. I've bin taken on as cabin boy on a trawler, leaving early Sunday morning. I just want to thank you for all you did for me. Please give the other letter to my father and ask him not to think to badly of me. You've both been good freinds to me.*
>
> "*Yours faithfully, Baz Caldwell.*"

Immy looked up at the sound of Sarah Bray's snivelling.

"That's not going to do any good, is it?" she snapped. "I'm sorry, but you have no idea what this is going to do to my father. How *could* you have let him do this?"

"You can't blame us, miss!" Enoch railed back as Sarah snivelled louder. "The boy had a mind of his own, and sure as God made apples he was never meant to be a shopkeeper."

"So you thought you could do better for him by filling his head with tales of adventure at sea? For what? So he could go to sea on a stinking trawler ship!"

"What the devil's going on in here?"

They all heard Quentin's voice at the same time, and Immy spun around to see her father filling the rear doorway. Against the bright sunlight outside he looked large and menacing, and Mrs Bray gasped and clung to her husband.

Immy's stomach was knotted now, and she could have bitten out her tongue for her viciousness. It wasn't Sarah's fault.

"Come into the sitting-room, please, where we can all discuss this more sensibly," she said quickly, taking charge before her father could get another word in.

"Would someone tell me what's going on?" Quentin thundered as he followed them, not at all pleased at having his Sunday afternoon disrupted. "Who are these people, Imogen? And where's Baz?"

"I don't want to sit like comp'ny, beggin' your pardon," Sarah mumbled. "I want to go home."

"So you will, my duck," Enoch told her roughly. "Just as soon as we do what we came here for."

"And that is?" Quentin snapped.

"Father, I think you should hear what Mr Bray has got to say. There's a letter for you from Baz."

"A *letter*? What's all this? Has the boy got literary aspirations now?" Quentin was full of sarcasm.

He took the letter silently and ripped it open, and then his face darkened. He didn't say anything for a few moments, which was worse than if he'd exploded with rage. Then he turned on the unfortunate Brays.

"Did you know about this? Have you been hatching up this scheme with my boy all this time?"

"I have not, sir!" Enoch shouted back. "'Tis as much of a shock to me and my old lady as 'tis to you, and she's fair shook up about it. She loved that boy."

"And so did I," Quentin rasped.

Sarah Bray spoke up hoarsely. "The sea was his life, Mr Caldwell, sir, and everybody knew that. There was never no holding him, not when his heart was so set on it."

She stumbled over the words awkwardly, unused to voicing her feelings. But the statement was eloquent enough.

"We have to accept that, Father," Immy said quietly. "This had to come someday."

"But not yet. He's only a boy. Only fifteen. He's still a child." He drew a deep breath, aware that he was in danger of showing how raw his feelings were to these two. And it wasn't done. Even now, in the midst of his heartbreak at what he saw as losing another of his children, he remembered his dignity.

"This has been a shock, Mr Bray," he said harshly. "But I've always been a fair man, and I know my son was doing a job he favoured. He's done wrong to leave like this, but I cast no blame at your door."

"Thank you, sir," Enoch said in obvious relief. "Then we'll be off. 'Tis a pity, though. He were a good 'un, and I'll have to be looking round for another ferry-lad now."

Immy ushered them out quickly before her father could throw a fit at such crass insensitivity. From his set face, she knew his sarcastic tone hid his true feelings.

"Oh well, that puts it all into perspective, doesn't it? I've lost a son and he's lost a ferry-lad."

"You haven't lost Baz," she said, putting her arms around him. "You'll never lose any of us."

"No? Think about it, Imogen. Daisy and Teddy are settled in Weston with your aunt and uncle. Elsie – well, she may still live here for a time, but she'll be closer to Joe than any of us now, and rightly so, of course. And now Baz."

"And then there was one," Immy said, echoing his thoughts. "You've still got me, Daddy."

"Thank God for that," he said, his arms tense around her.

Her eyes were blurred and troubled, however. Because what did that make her? The last one at home. The spinster daughter, dutifully staying at home to care for a widowed father, the last relic of a time long past...

She shook off the feeling, knowing it was unworthy. Besides, her father wasn't old. He wasn't yet fifty, and although she was quite sure he wouldn't entertain the idea just now – and neither would any of his children – the day might come when he would even consider marrying again.

"Do you think you're up to telling the others what's happened yet, Father?" she said, before her thoughts travelled too far along that uneasy road.

"I suppose it has to be done. I still can't condone the boy's actions for going off like that, but—"

"But would you have agreed if he'd come to you and suggested it?" she said shrewdly. "It's not exactly running away. You must admit that he's shown a lot of backbone."

"I do admit it," Quentin said. "Perhaps I've got too stuffy in my old age to remember what a spirit of adventure is like. We had it in abundance in the last war, and folk have become spineless since then."

"Whatever you are, Daddy, you're not old!"

Immy refused to even think about war making men out of boys.

Later, when the telling was done, and the outrage had been dealt with, it became obvious that the Marys didn't think Quentin was old, either. But then, they were all of a similar age. They had gone through a war, not together, but with similar experiences. And they had all known bereavement.

While Elsie was indignant over the sneaky way Baz had done this, and Joe was pointing out that it could be worse because Baz was alive and happy, doing something he had always wanted to do, the Marys were sympathising with Quentin, and putting the smile back on his face.

There was something to be said for the companionship of like-minded people, Immy thought. She resolved to invite them downstairs more often. It wasn't that they had shut them away or that the Marys had chosen voluntary isolation, like forgotten pictures in the attic... But they just hadn't socialised much.

Until now.

And if they ever had to share the intimacy of the air-raid shelter that stood like a sentinel at the bottom of the garden and was now tastefully covered with earth and plants, all discreetly held in place with chicken wire, then perhaps they should all get better acquainted.

–

Daisy was also thinking about new acquaintances. The news that her sister Elsie had just got engaged had filled her romantic heart with all sorts of thoughts. She had told Lucy about it in her last letter. Lucy was now allowed to write back, and they exchanged the kind of secrets in letters that you couldn't seem to say face to face, even with your dearest friend.

Daisy, of course, had now discovered enough about life to know a bit more than most girls her age. Some of her new friends at the hospital had told her plenty, and it was a nurse's duty to know everything, she told Lucy loftily.

"*I wonder if they've done it*," she wrote.

> "*I can't imagine our Elsie getting all hot and bothered, somehow, but Joe's nice enough to persuade her. What do you think? If they're going to get married quite soon, do you think she'd go to hell if they did it beforehand?*"

"*You're a wicked person to even think of such a thing, Daisy Caldwell*," Lucy wrote back.

> "*But if it was me, and he was as nice as you say, I might. Only might, mind you.*
>
> "*I've never met anyone like that, and I'm not likely to while I'm stuck in here. By the way, they say I'm progressing nicely, whatever that means. I miss you. Why aren't you telling me more about this Cal person? Would he get you all hot and bothered, do you think?*"

Daisy laughed at that. Their letters were of the grasshopper variety, jumping from one topic to another in random fashion, as cosy as if they were sitting beside one another. It was just as well, though, that nobody saw the letters but themselves.

She reflected on Cal a bit more. Would he get her hot and bothered? Did he do that already? He certainly made her heart go pit-a-pat whenever she saw him, but she didn't feel the storming surge of passion that some of the older nurses told her about, teasing her and calling her Miss Greenery.

Thinking about *that* made her heart beat faster. Passion was another of those lovely words you never used, but which apparently was important when you were in love.

Daisy sighed. Obviously, she wasn't in love yet. Or if she was, it was only growing very slowly. Perhaps it would help if she could meet Cal alone, but so far it hadn't happened. It was such a long-distance affair that it wasn't an affair at all.

"There's someone asking for you, Daisy-Daisy," one of the older nurses said on Friday afternoon, at the end of her working day. "I think you've been holding out on us!"

"Asking for me?" Her thoughts went at once to her family. Something had happened to her father. Or Baz had been hauled back to Bristol. Or Immy had had an accident…or Elsie…or *Teddy*…

"Come on, you dark horse," the nurse teased her. "I know what a young man's after when he's got a certain light in his eyes. *And* looking all slick and Brylcreemed, too."

Daisy's face flooded with colour. Cal. It had to be Cal. But coming here, to the hospital where she worked, especially to see her! To ask for her! If her heart wasn't thudding fast enough to start up a steam engine now, she didn't know what would.

"Bye, Winnie," she said in a stifled voice, racing out of the hospital with the nurse's laughter following her.

He was there. Standing by the stone wall alongside the pavement and looking somehow brash and sheepish at the same time. She stopped racing when she saw him and tried to behave like a young lady should.

"I guessed it was you," she said inanely.

"Did you? I didn't know whether you might have thought it was someone else."

"No; why should I?" She wondered frantically where the easy rapport between them had gone. They'd had no trouble conversing on the beach when he'd bought her an ice-cream that first day, so why did it seem as if they were oceans apart, even though there was only a couple of feet between them?

"I thought you might have some other caller."

It was such a quaintly old-fashioned way of putting it that an intuition worthy of someone older than herself flashed through Daisy. He was just as nervous as she was. Boys got nervous, too. Even boys who usually dressed in men's uniforms and played at being soldiers or pilots. She could see it from the small twitch at the side of his mouth. And he was here without the prop of that uniform or the regulation sports outfit and the support of his fellow erks…

"I don't have any callers at all," she said, smiling sweetly. "Anyway, I'm not sure my aunt and uncle would want me to have one, unless we had been properly introduced. Or unless I asked a certain person home with me for them to look over."

"And would you ever feel like asking a certain person home for them to look over?" he said, his face relaxing into a half-nervous smile.

Daisy felt her heart sing. She had flirted harmlessly with customers at her father's shop, but it hadn't meant a thing. Her sisters had called her a silly girl and indulged her for it. But this was different.

This was teasing in a far more delightful way, a kind of hedging around one another because they both wanted to see one another again. It was obvious, or why would Cal have come here especially?

"Well, I might," she said. "What do you think?"

"I think you should. I definitely think you should get your aunt and uncle's approval; otherwise, how could a certain person ever ask a certain young lady to go to the pictures with him one evening?"

Chapter Fifteen

Teddy loved talking on the telephone. He loved it when Aunt Rose handed it over to him, and he could talk to his sister Immy just as if she was in the room. He especially loved it when she promised to come and see him some-time soon and said that she might take him out in their Daddy's car.

"You and the other little boys," Immy said generously, praying than none of them would feel ill. "And Daisy, of course, if she wants to come."

"Our Daisy won't come. She'll be out with her boy," Teddy said importantly.

Imogen stared at the wall above the telephone for a few seconds, thinking it really was time they changed the cabbage-rose wallpaper that was fading in the sunlight. Pausing before she answered, so that she could organise her thoughts properly before she asked.

"What boy, Teddy?"

She heard her small brother snigger. "The one who's going to fly an aeroplane. He's called Cal, and he came here with our Daisy the other day, and Aunt Rose gave him some tea, and said they could go to the pictures together."

"Oh, *did* she?"

Imogen couldn't decide whether she was more annoyed that she didn't know anything about this, or astonished that Daisy was actually walking out with a boy. At her age. A whole three years younger than Immy herself!

"Teddy, let me talk to Aunt Rose again, please," she said imperiously.

"But I want to tell you about George and the hedgehog," he howled at once.

"I don't want to hear about George and the hedgehog. I want to speak to Aunt Rose."

"I don't like you anymore," he said, sulking.

"I'll hear all about it another time, poppet. I promise. Now, will you *please* let me speak to Aunt Rose!"

She was trying hard to hold on to her patience when she heard her aunt's laughing voice on the phone.

"He's a card, isn't he, Immy?"

"Oh yes. Now then, Aunt Rose, what's all this about Daisy seeing a boy?" Immy asked, forestalling a long discussion of Teddy's antics. "Do we know him?"

"My goodness, dear, you do sound like a headmistress! He's a very nice young man serving as a cadet with the Royal Air Force at Locking Camp, and of course we know him."

She was liberal with the truth and saw no reason to reveal that Daisy had met him first – she had got the full facts out of her niece now. But she also prided herself on being a shrewd judge of character, and she would certainly vouch for Air Cadet Callum Monks.

"And you've agreed to them going to the pictures?"

She bit her lip at her aunt's continuing hoot, beginning to realise that she did indeed sound like a headmistress, or a disapproving spinster aunt. It wasn't a comparison that charmed her.

"Immy dear, don't take on so. Daisy is a very well-adjusted young girl, and I promise you neither your uncle nor I have any qualms about the propriety of the invitation. Cal will bring her home afterwards and stay for some supper before going back to camp. It's all perfectly proper."

As the voice became a little sharper, Immy realised she was in danger of offending her aunt and questioning her ability to look after Daisy at all.

"I'm sorry, Aunt Rose. I never doubted you for a minute. It was just a bit of a surprise to hear Teddy blurt it out like that. I've been feeling a little over-protective since Baz went off," she invented wildly, "and wondering if I've been looking after the younger ones in the way Mother would have expected."

She closed her eyes, knowing guiltily that she had been thinking of no such thing, and glad there was no one else in the house to hear such a glib and shameful reply.

"I understand, my love, but you needn't worry on that score. Your mother would be proud of all of you," Rose said more gently. "And you're welcome to come here any time to talk to Daisy about it – though I suggest you don't make it too obvious. She's always been high-spirited, but she's growing up now, and wouldn't take too kindly to it."

"Perhaps it would be a good idea if we all came down one weekend," Immy said at once. "It's ages since Father's been to Weston, and he and Mother always did love the seaside."

"You can come here whenever you like, darling. Our door is always open, you know that."

It was silly to let the news that Daisy was walking out with a young man affect her, or make her feel so restless, Immy thought as she replaced the receiver. And she knew that for all Aunt Rose's seemingly relaxed attitude, she would keep a very keen eye on Daisy and this Callum Monks who was going to fly aeroplanes.

She heard the sound of creaking floorboards above, and knew the Marys would be having afternoon tea, their ritual at four o'clock every afternoon. She knew she would be welcome to join them if she knocked at their door – and a few minutes later, without even knowing why, she found herself doing just that.

"Well, isn't this nice!" Mary Yard said, beaming. "We were just talking about your sister, Imogen dear, and wondering what we could buy her as a gift."

Immy looked blank, until she realised they were talking about Elsie and a wedding present.

"It's very sweet of you to think of buying her anything at all. I'm sure she won't expect it."

"Then it will be all the nicer for being unexpected, won't it? Now then, what little problem is creasing that lovely brow of yours?"

Mary Baxter poured them each a cup of tea, and the older women sat expectantly on either side of the fireplace – a bit like matching bookends, Immy thought irreverently.

"What makes you think I've got a problem of any size?" she asked, taking a sip of tea far too quickly, and wincing as it scalded her mouth.

Mary Yard laughed. "Oh, come now. When a pretty young lady prefers to spend her time with two old codgers like us on a lovely summer's afternoon, there has to be something afoot!"

"You're not old codgers!" Immy protested, pinking.

But it was true. They were always smartly dressed, their hair always immaculate, their fingernails buffed and neat.

It was a shame neither of them had thought to marry again, but it said something for the depth of their feelings for their first loves.

Immy moved her thoughts quickly away from the unwelcome idea that downstairs was a widower who could do worse. She did *not* want to think of that.

"So what do you have on your mind, Imogen?" Mary Baxter prompted again.

"Have you ever been to Weston-super-Mare?" she said, not really knowing where the question came from.

"Once, a long time ago. We went on the train, didn't we, Mary?" she asked her friend. "It was such a happy day out, and we'd never seen such lovely golden sand."

The other woman nodded, her eyes unblinking.

"Is everyone well there, Imogen?"

"Oh yes, they're fine, evacuees and all. My sister Daisy's actually met a young man, and my aunt's agreed to let them go to the pictures together."

Oh God, she *did* sound like a headmistress or a disapproving spinster aunt now.

"Ah," said Mary Yard. "And you think you're being left behind, is that it?"

For a moment Immy was angry at the assumption, and then she had to admit that it was exactly how she felt.

As if such things mattered when the country was in such turmoil over the imminence of war, with an inept government seemingly powerless to stop it. Those matters should be the most important things in a patriot's life.

But they weren't. The two things were completely unrelated, and at this moment, politics were of no importance to a person who didn't know what life had in store for her anymore. Whose life had once been so ordered and so settled, with a darling mother and a stalwart father,

249

and a loving family all around her…and childhood not so far behind…

To her horror she found the cup shaking in her hands. The next minute it had been taken from her and she was being held in Mary Baxter's arms.

"Tell us what's really wrong, Imogen. We don't like to see you like this. It's so unlike you. You're usually so bright and cheerful. You are happy about Elsie's engagement, aren't you, dear?"

Immy gulped back the tears, feeling very foolish.

"Of course I am. I'm very fond of Joe, and I know they'll be happy – providing Mr Hitler lets them be," she added, crossing her fingers as she spoke the name, the way everyone did.

"And from what we've heard of your aunt, she'll keep a weather eye on Daisy," Mary Yard put in. "But my guess is that you feel a bit put out because they've both found a new interest, and you haven't. Isn't that it?"

"Perhaps it is," Immy said reluctantly, knowing darned well that it was. "Perhaps I'm just plain jealous – and that's silly, and a bit shameful, isn't it?"

"Of course not. It's perfectly natural. But what about that friend you were telling us about – she doesn't have a beau, does she? And goodness me, the two of you are still very young. What age are you both – nineteen?"

"Twenty. And no, Helen doesn't have a young man. But it doesn't concern her too much." Not after Robert Preston…

"There you are, then. You take a leaf out of her book and make the most of your youth. Enjoy being carefree young girls together. There's plenty of time for falling in love."

"My parents were married very young, and so were both of you, weren't you?" Immy pointed out.

Immediately she wished she hadn't, as a shadow fell over both their faces. She felt she had been far too intrusive. But Mary Yard's quiet words suggested no offence had been taken.

"That was out of necessity, dear. We all had to snatch at happiness while we could in those days, because we never knew how long it would last."

In the sudden silence, the only sound was the ticking of the grandfather clock in the corner of the room, beating with monotonous regularity. All three of them were thinking the same thing. Time was rushing them towards the inevitable again, when no one knew how long happiness was going to last.

"I think I'll pay Helen a visit. I haven't seen her in a while, and she'll be tickled pink at Daisy's new pash," Immy said quickly. "I doubt it will last, anyway. They never do."

Much as she had felt that the Marys' apartment was a small refuge a short while ago, now she wanted to get out of there, feeling oddly stifled by the rich perfume of the potted plants and the onerous ticking of that darned clock. Ticking time away. Ticking life away...

She got out her bicycle and pedalled like fury towards the part of town where Helen lived. Earlier that afternoon, it had been lovely and sunny, but predictably for English weather, long before she reached the Church house the rain had pelted down.

She felt a straggly mess by the time she pressed their front door bell, but was prepared to put on a clownish grin, knowing Helen would see the funny side of her appearance. Shaking the drops from her hair, she pushed the bell again.

The door flew open and an irritated voice told her it only needed pushing once, not fifty times. And then the voice stopped, and its owner gaped at Immy.

"Good God, Imogen, you do look a sketch!"

"James!" she stammered. "What are you doing here?"

He started to laugh. "I live here, remember? For heaven's sake, come inside – but do try not to drip all over the Persian carpet, or my mother will have a blue fit."

"I thought you were away driving tanks or whatever it is you do," she said, feeling ridiculously disorientated and out of breath from battling against the elements. "And where's Helen?"

He caught her arm and pulled her inside. She felt incapable of moving, even though the rain was beginning to drive into the hallway. And she was indeed dripping. The rain clung in rivulets to her skin and her hair hung in rats' tails on her shoulders. Water ran off the hem of her frock, and her shoes were sodden. How could this all have happened in so short a time? She wondered, bemused.

"Are you all right? You look pretty seedy to me." His voice came swimmingly towards her.

She blinked. "I'm perfectly all right," she said crossly. She had no intention of swooning like some Victorian heroine when faced with a young man she had known all her life, even if he looked quite unlike himself now.

That was a thought that had no place in her head either. She asked quickly for a towel to rid herself of some of the drips.

"And where is Helen?" she asked again, as if it was of paramount importance.

"Helen and the parents are out, so you'll just have to make do with me. You'd better come up to the bathroom and dry yourself off properly, and then I'll make us some tea."

Her instinct was to ask him if he knew how, since she presumed the servants did it for him. Then she realised how ungracious that would be, when he was being so kind and understanding. But it also occurred to her that she was alone in the house with a very handsome young man, and her father certainly wouldn't approve, even knowing of James's integrity.

"Look, perhaps I'd better go," she said.

"Rot. You're in no state to be cycling home again, and just look at the way the rain's coming down now."

His eyes challenged her. "What's the matter, old thing? Don't you trust me? I assure you my intentions are honourable. Disgustingly and boringly so, if you must know. I'm not in the habit of seducing my sister's little friends."

Immy's face went scarlet. If he only knew how that bruised and wounded her. Not that she *wanted* him to seduce her, nor had she ever thought of him in that way, but to know that he only thought of her as his sister's "little friend" was the worst possible humiliation.

"You don't think of me as a scarlet woman, then?" she found herself saying through chattering teeth as he led her upstairs to the bathroom and offered her a selection of large fluffy towels. She was trying to be provocative but knew she had failed miserably. It was hard to flirt when you knew your hair was dripping and your frock was clinging to you everywhere it touched.

He laughed. "Good God, no. More as an old chum."

"Good. Then get out of here and let me try to repair the rain damage," she told him crisply. She could still hear him laughing as she shut the bathroom door and shot the bolt.

She sat on the edge of the bath, feeling all kinds of a fool for saying what she had. It was all thanks to Helen for saying James would marry her like a shot and that they could be sisters.

She jumped a few minutes later when she heard him tap on the bathroom door, and her heart pounded like a drum.

"In case you think you still look too disreputable for polite company, I suggest you put on the bathrobe behind the door and then go along to Helen's room to borrow one of her frocks. I'm sure she won't mind – and the tea will be brewed in ten minutes."

"Thank you," Immy croaked.

Thank God he couldn't read her mind. Thank God he hadn't realised that for one wild moment she had thought he might be going to make some seductive suggestion. And thank God he would never know that for an even smaller moment, she had toyed with the idea of what it would be like...

Ten minutes later, scrubbed and tidied, and wearing one of Helen's day frocks, she presented herself in the Church dining-room. She sipped the welcome cup of tea he had made – brewed to perfection, she told him airily.

Her hair was still damp, and as she gave an unavoidable sneeze, he offered to rub it dry for her.

"It's not necessary," she said hastily.

"Sit, and behave," he ordered, just as her mother used to when she was a child. Just as Teddy had begun ordering the boisterous George about, she thought, with the glimmer of laughter in her eyes.

But she sat and behaved, and James stood behind her and rubbed her long hair dry with a towel, raking it gently with his fingers until the natural waves returned, and sending unexpected waves of pleasure rushing through her.

She couldn't be sure, but as he lifted the weight of her hair off the nape of her neck, she thought she felt the touch of something far warmer than his fingers on her skin. But he couldn't have kissed her – could he?

Not an old chum like her. She must have been mistaken.

"Right, that will do. I'll fetch you a comb so you can make yourself look respectable again," he said abruptly. "The folks will be back soon, and they won't want to see you looking as if you've been pulled through a hedge."

"Thank you, James. You're a pal," Immy said sincerely. "You'll make some girl a great husband one of these days."

"I might, when she's ready to be asked," he said.

"You've met her, then?" she asked.

"I didn't say that."

"You didn't answer the question either," she pointed out, her spirits revived.

"That's because some questions are best left unanswered," he said enigmatically.

He left her to ponder on that and brought her back a comb, but she only gave her hair token attention, knowing it would fall naturally into place anyway. She was far more interested in what he was saying – and what he *wasn't* saying.

"*So?* Have you met Miss Right?" she persisted.

He laughed. "Have you and Helen ever thought of starting one of those matrimonial agencies?"

"Certainly not. I think it's an awful idea."

But she was becoming more exhilarated by the minute now. It was always fun talking to one of the Churches. Few things got them down – disregarding the unfortunate affair with Robert Preston, of course. But James didn't know about that, and Helen seemed to have recovered fully.

"I hear your sister's become engaged," he said casually. "Nice fellow, is he?"

"Very nice. And you're avoiding the issue."

"My dear sweet Miss Caldwell, you must allow a gentleman some privacy regarding matters of the heart," he said teasingly.

She laughed with him and caught her breath as she saw just what a very personable young man he really was. She had never considered it before. She idly considered it now…and then common sense rushed back, reminding her that if this was a reaction to her sisters' new attachments, it was in very poor taste.

"I think I'd better go," she said in some confusion. "The rain's stopped, and if you'll explain to Helen what's happened, I'll bundle my frock into a paper bag and bring hers back tomorrow. She'll be here then, I suppose?"

"She will, but I won't. I was only home on a forty-eight-hour pass, and it's up tonight."

"Oh Lord, James, I haven't even asked you anything about your tank. What is it like?"

"Big, hot, noisy, smelly – and exciting," he answered.

"Well, at least that got some reaction!"

"I'll be able to tell you more when I've been in action in my Bertha," he said.

"Bertha? Does everyone have names for them?" she said, starting to laugh.

"God knows, but I do. It makes her more human, and we'll all be needing a bit of humanity when we take our killing machines into battle."

He was suddenly serious, and she didn't want him to be. He was one of the frivolous Church siblings, whose family had money and position, and could always make her laugh. Fair-haired, handsome and a dear friend...and as if his words had given her a glimpse of some nameless horror, she had a wild urge to cling to him and wish him God speed.

She didn't, of course. Instead, she leaned towards him lightly, and pecked him on the cheek, the way old chums did.

"Well, I wish you happy times with your old tank, James, and I'll dream of sweeter things."

"And so will I," she thought she heard him say softly as she whirled out of the door.

She phoned Helen later that evening, with many apologies for borrowing her frock.

"Don't worry, old thing," Helen said, laughing. "James entertained us royally, describing the state you were in. I'm sorry I missed it. We had to go to a meeting of one of Mother's fund-raising committees, and Father came along to add weight. Anyway, you're invited to tea tomorrow, so you can tell me all the gossip then. We'll be in the doldrums, since James will have gone back to his regiment, so you can cheer us up."

"I'm not sure about that, but I'll do my best," Immy said, realising other people had worse troubles than she did. Well, hardly worse, but different, she amended.

Talk of war was getting really serious now, and young men of a certain age were becoming resigned to the fact that either that they were going to be conscripted or would have to volunteer anyway. Patriotism was running high and was likely to increase.

Immy was glad Baz was too young to even think about it, but she knew Elsie lived on a knife edge of anxiety, wondering if Joe would think it his duty to volunteer before waiting to be called up. Many of his peers did. It was a *man* thing, Daisy would have said dramatically.

It was Daisy that she wanted to talk to Helen about, but by the next afternoon the unworthy thoughts of jealousy had vanished, and she could laugh at herself.

"I felt like driving straight down there and sorting the young madam out," she told her, relaxing in Helen's garden.

"Honestly, Immy, you are starting to sound – well, a little *elderly*, darling!"

"*Elderly?*"

Helen wouldn't be deterred. "You know what Daisy's like. She's always flirted. It doesn't mean anything. And I'm quite sure your aunt has vetted the boy very carefully."

Immy was still smarting over the word "elderly" to take too much notice of her friend's reassurance.

"I'm not being *elderly*. I'm just concerned for my sister, and I think you of all people should know the dangers of flirting, Helen."

"That's really hitting below the belt, darling!"

"That's just what I mean – *darling*."

For a moment the tension between them was palpable, and then Helen's mouth broke into a grin, and she reached across and squeezed Immy's hand.

"I'm an idiot, aren't I? I dare say if I'd been the oldest in the family and had younger sisters instead of an older brother who's always looked after me, I'd be concerned too. But you really shouldn't take on the role of mother and saint all rolled into one, Immy. You should let go of them and remember that you have a life to live too."

Immy stared unseeingly down the length of the lovely garden, so heavily perfumed now that it almost stunned the senses and wondered.

"I'm certainly no saint. Nor would I want to be."

"You're not their mother either – and I make no apology for reminding you of your darling Frances. I'll tell you what. Let's put a wager on who finds a young man first – and gets the first kiss."

Immy began to laugh. "Oh, yes? It's easy for you, going to all those functions with your parents and meeting eligible bachelors. What chance do I have, stuck in the office with the portly Kenneth Harris?"

"Well, you could always consider him, of course."

"What: old, fat and forty? I'd have to be desperate," Immy retorted with a giggle. She felt much revived by Helen's company.

"We'll give a trip to the cinema as first prize. Winner's treat. Oh, and by the way, James doesn't count," Helen went on relentlessly.

"What's that supposed to mean?" Immy said, her heart giving a leap for no reason at all.

"In the wager. You can't count falling for James as a possibility, because it would be all too easy."

"Would it?"

"Of course. You know he's always had a thing for you, don't you? A pash. A crush. Whatever you like to call it.

Only being James, of course, he'll never show it. He'll just pine in secret. But I know. Sisters always do."

She was laughing, but Immy suddenly felt upset. She didn't want to think of James pining away with a secret "pash" on her. It sounded so shallow. If it had to be anything at all, it had to be the real thing.

She wasn't sure that she wanted that either, though. He was like a brother to her, and it was incestuous to think of falling in love with your brother. It wasn't right.

"I think that's nonsense," she said crossly. "Anyway, nobody could look less like pining away than James. He's got the physique of an ox."

"You've noticed, then," Helen said archly.

There was something about her tone that made Immy suspicious. "I've noticed your little scheme! You're trying to put me off the most obvious in order to win your own wager! So who's your victim? There *is* someone, isn't there?"

"Maybe. Probably not. Well, Mother's organising a dance at the end of August to raise money for servicemen's comforts. We've been discussing it this weekend, and one of the men on the committee is rather nice, that's all."

She paused. "The trouble is, they all seem nice at first, don't they, Immy?"

Her voice faltered, and Immy knew she was remembering Robert Preston.

"They're not all the same, darling. I told you that before, didn't I?"

"You just remember that about Daisy's young man, then, and trust her to behave. She comes from good stock, anyway."

"Like a filly – and just as flighty," Immy said, and they began laughing again.

Chapter Sixteen

As July merged into August, Quentin received a second letter by post from his son. It outlined Baz's guilt and sorrow at upsetting his family by his departure but assured them that he was well and thought of them all constantly.

Quentin had had to accept many things in his life – not least the traumatic death of his beloved wife, and the loss of the business he had so proudly built up. He had weathered it all with stoicism, and he wasn't going to let his son's misdemeanour affect that resolve. He knew the only way to save face was to accept the fact that Baz had probably fulfilled his destiny, so he had decided to praise the boy's ingenuity and sense of adventure instead.

"I'm sure he's having a high old time by now, and good luck to him," he told his cronies at his club. "It takes a man's courage to recognise his destiny and do what the boy did. And naturally I blame myself for being short-sighted enough to ever think he could be a shopkeeper. No, Baz was always a seaman in the making."

The more he said the words, the more he made himself believe them. Whether or not his listeners believed them was another matter.

The Marys certainly did or were canny enough to say so for the sake of his dignity.

"Another slice of seed cake, Mr Caldwell?" Mary Yard said, when he joined her at four o'clock on Saturday afternoon, alone for once since Mary Baxter was out visiting.

"I believe I will, Mary. And I'd be honoured if you would call me Quentin. Youngsters don't stand on ceremony these days, and it seems foolish for us to do so. Especially as it's more than likely we'll need to share the confines of the air-raid shelter in the days to come."

"It looks very much that way, and I agree that there'll be little point in standing on formality then," Mary said quietly. "We remember the last time, don't we?"

"We do indeed," Quentin said grimly. "And none of us ever thought it would come again. What a cruel farce it was to call it the war to end all wars. That statement was the biggest invention in history!…I beg your pardon for getting so heated, Mary."

She put her hand over his. There was a pleasing scent of lavender about her, Quentin thought approvingly.

"There's no need to apologise. Evil men will always want what they can't have, and that includes trampling over other countries, no matter how many lives they take in the process."

"How perceptive you are," he said, patting her hand with his other one. "It's relaxing to talk to you, Mary."

Then, as if realising how close they were, he drew back at once, and saw her blush a delicate pink. She turned away and busied herself with pouring more tea.

At this rate, he'd be awash with it, he thought, but felt no inclination to go back downstairs yet. Everyone was out, and he was almost surprised to discover how much he enjoyed this easy and uncomplicated companionship. It was good to have a woman to talk to, other than his daughters.

"It's because we're of an age," Mary said gently, echoing his thoughts. "We don't share personal memories, but we do share memories of that other war, and it's natural to dread what will happen in the next one. We know what to expect."

"But do we? I don't think we have any idea of what's to come. I think this will be a very different war."

He hadn't meant to alarm her, but he saw her hands shake, and she spoke in a more impassioned way.

"However different it is, it comes down to the same in terms of human suffering. Mothers will lose their sons, and wives and sweethearts will lose their menfolk. Nothing can be more terrible than that. Women are always the losers in the end, no matter how great the victory."

Her trembling had become greater now, and she bowed her head so he wouldn't see the tears that were normally locked up inside and weren't for public viewing.

"Mary, my dear, I didn't mean to upset you," Quentin said, embarrassed and appalled. He squeezed her hand again.

She said nothing for a moment, then raised her flushed face to his.

"You didn't, and I'm a foolish old woman to take on so."

"Whatever you are, you're not old," Quentin said, with a feeble attempt at gallantry. "I respect you for still having such feelings after all this time."

"Why wouldn't I? Once you love somebody, it's for life. You never lose those feelings, do you?"

"Of course not," he said, removing his hand and wondering if he had intruded too far upon a private grief.

His own feelings for Frances were as deep as ever, though he had long since admitted to himself that it had been years since she had been a proper wife to him. But her illness had claimed her faculties, and he had never blamed her for it, nor asked for anything different. He had been content to care for her as lovingly as he could – but a man was still a man for all that. There had been times when he had yearned to take her in his arms and feel her respond to his passion as she had done in the heady, early days of their marriage.

When he realised where his thoughts were going, he stood up awkwardly. He had been ensconced in this cosy atmosphere for too long, and far from comforting him, it had suddenly begun to stifle him.

"Time I made a move and watered the garden," he said.

"High time," Mary said steadily, and he knew very well she had followed his wayward thoughts just as clearly as if he had said them out loud.

–

The invitation came in the morning post, although Helen could just as easily have handed it to Immy herself. She opened it curiously, taking out the gilt-edged card inside and gaping at the printed words before reading Helen's scribbled note.

> *Before you say no, Immy, think about our wager!*
> *You can look over You-know-who, and also see if*
> *anyone takes your fancy. Do say yes. It will be such*
> *a lark!*

"What have you got there?" Elsie asked her sister, who had been silent for some moments.

"It's an invitation to one of Mrs Church's fund-raising dances for servicemen's comforts on August the twenty-sixth. I don't think I shall go. I'd be right out of my element."

"Of course you must go! It's a chance to see how the other half lives, if nothing else."

"Exactly. All those chinless wonders and bright young debs. I'd have nothing in common with them, and I'd stick out like a sore thumb."

"Immy, for goodness' sake! You're becoming far too insular lately. You hardly ever go anywhere, and you certainly don't have Baz's adventurous spirit. I'd really like to see you spread your wings a bit more, and this might be just the opportunity."

"This sounds far too much like the happily engaged sister dying to play the matchmaker."

Elsie laughed. "Well, hardly, since I haven't been invited to this posh do. Where is it, anyway?"

"It's in Bath, at a large hotel. Knowing Helen, she'll probably suggest that we all stay overnight."

Elsie's smile widened. "All the more reason for taking a chance then, you ninny. Who knows who you may bump into along a dark hotel corridor?"

Over his eggs and bacon, Quentin had been half listening to the banter for the last five minutes. Following Elsie's teasing words, he closed his morning newspaper with all its grim news, feeling that he must say his piece.

"I think that's enough of that, Elsie. But there is another little matter, of course. There's the fact that Imogen hasn't asked what I might think about her accepting the invitation to a dance, *and* possibly staying in a hotel overnight." He paused as Immy drew in her breath.

"*Do* you object, Father?" she said, knowing that if he did, it would definitely turn the tables on her hesitancy about accepting the invitation. Contrary to the last, as Aunt Rose would say...

"I was about to say that I don't think it's such a bad idea to have one or two frivolous evenings while you can, darling. Mrs Church is an admirable fund-raiser, so it's all in a good cause, and who knows when such times may come again?"

"Oh, Daddy, don't say that," Elsie said quickly, knowing what he was implying.

"It's no use burying our heads in the sand, my love. The news is dire. The ARP wardens are already insisting that we prepare our black-out curtains, and they'll be around to inspect them soon. We can't hide from it any longer."

At her crestfallen face, he added with a small attempt at humour: "Cheer up, Elsie. Think of the silver lining as far as Preston's is concerned. We're already doing a roaring trade in selling black-out material. If it's good for business it puts money in Joe's pocket, doesn't it?"

"I'd rather know that Joe was safe at home than gloating over profits for the shop, and planning on going to war," Elsie burst out, and rushed from the dining-room before anyone could say anything else.

Immy made to go after her, but her father stopped her.

"No. Leave her, Imogen. She needs to deal with things in her own way, the same as we all do. And what I think you should do, my love, is to accept your friend's invitation, and have a thoroughly good time."

"And should I stay at the hotel overnight, if Helen suggests it?"

"Absolutely," her father said.

Why she should think it so daring, Immy couldn't think. It made her cross to be unable to stop prevaricating. Where was her backbone, her strength of character?

She called Helen on the telephone before she could change her mind and told her she would love to come.

"Wonderful!" Helen said in delight. "And since we'll have danced the night away, we're going to stay at the hotel until Sunday. Mother's already booked our rooms, so you can share with me. Our treat, of course – and it'll be such fun, Immy. You're not going to argue about that, are you?"

"Good Lord, no. Whatever made you think I would!"

She put down the receiver. Now that it was done, she started immediately panicking about what she was going to wear. She had nothing suitable at all. She didn't go to fund-raising dances organised by the elite.

"I've done it," she told her father as he came out of the dining-room. "Helen's ecstatic."

"Good. So should you be. And before you say anything else, I've had an idea. You may not be comfortable with it, but I want you to hear me out."

On Sunday, Immy made her long-promised visit to see the family – and especially to see Daisy. During the journey she kept going over that last emotional chat with her father. She would never have dreamed of asking him for what he'd offered in a million years, nor would she have expected him to suggest it.

Once she had recovered from the usual exuberant greetings from Teddy and the boys, admired George's new antics and learned of his tentative friendship with the hedgehog in the garden, she managed to get her aunt alone. Daisy was out for the afternoon, but she was expected back about four o'clock, and bringing Cal for tea. So the inspection must wait.

"You can't imagine what my father's done," she said to Rose bluntly.

"Well, since I can't imagine it, you'll have to tell me, won't you? I'm sure it can't be anything too dreadful, though. Quentin was always a cautious man."

"It's not dreadful at all. It's — it's really rather wonderful," Immy confided, suddenly choked.

"My dear girl, this isn't at all like you!" Rose said in astonishment. "You'd better tell me at once."

As her aunt patted her back, Immy gulped, feeling more like a five-year-old than a responsible young woman of twenty.

"I'm going to a dance in Bath and staying at a hotel overnight with Helen and her parents. It will be a very posh affair, and Father said I should wear something really beautiful. Then he opened the closet where Mother kept her dance dresses and said I could choose whichever one I liked."

"My heavens! I thought he'd have got rid of them all."

Immy shook her head. "He couldn't bear to do that. They look just as beautiful as I remember them."

"But surely..." Rose spoke carefully, not wanting to offend her niece, and sensing how fragile she was now. "Aren't they a little dated, darling? Your mother hadn't danced for years before she became ill."

"That's the strangest thing, Aunt Rose. Stage costumes aren't the same as ordinary wear. They simply don't date in the same way. And you know the kind of thing Mother wore. All those lovely, gossamer dresses that we all adored."

Her voice trailed away, her mind's eye seeing her mother's sensual dancing, seeing Frances as she once was, slender and lovely and vibrant and alive…

"And have you chosen one of them to wear at this posh dance?" Rose's brisk voice penetrated her thoughts.

"Yes," Immy said. "Luckily, I'm the same size as Mother was before she got so thin. It's palest blue chiffon with silver threads running through it, and there are silver shoes to go with it."

"I remember." Rose nodded, blinking. "Has your father seen you in it, though? It might be too much for him."

"Actually, I think it released something inside him to see me try on the dress. I'd never want him, or any of us, to forget Mother, but he's kept all her things locked away, like a shrine to her memory. He hasn't really wanted to let any of us in, and I think it's been a good thing to bring those memories out into the open."

"And there speaks the wise child," Rose said.

Immy pulled a face. "Oh, I'm not wise. But I'm thrilled to have Mother's dress. Helen always wears such lovely clothes, and I didn't want to look like the poor relation."

Rose declined to say that whatever she wore, Imogen would always turn heads. Her striking colouring and mobile, expressive face would always do that. She was turning into a real beauty, even if she couldn't see it herself. Of course, all the Caldwell girls had inherited their mother's legendary beauty, Rose thought loyally.

The door opened, and Daisy came breezing into the room, bringing a welcome change from the charged atmosphere of the last few minutes. Behind her came a tall young man with an open face who was introduced as Callum Monks – Cal to his friends, he insisted with a smile.

"And you're stationed here at Locking, I understand?" Immy asked him.

"For the time being. Lord knows where we'll be sent when we've finished our training," he said, with all the pride of a young lion. "But as long as it's somewhere where I can get in plenty of flying hours, I'll be happy."

"There's not much doubt of that, my boy," Uncle Bertie said, coming indoors exhausted after romping in the garden with three small boys and a dog. "Once operations begin you'll go to wherever the powers that be decide to send you."

"Operations, indeed," Rose scoffed, as usual bringing the talk down to size. "Men's talk again!"

"At least it's better than Daisy's descriptions of hospital life, Mrs Painter," Cal said with a laugh. "Military operations are an honourable affair, but some of the things that go on inside a hospital are beyond talking about."

"Then we'll not talk about them today, thank you, Cal," Rose said, seeing that three small sets of ears had pricked up at the interesting thought of hearing anything gruesome.

She had begun to be far more careful of late, knowing how they got their small heads together to pick over any snippet of gossip. As bad as three little washerwomen, she thought, with real affection for them all.

Immy could see how well Cal was liked by the family here, and Daisy was clearly smitten. He passed, Immy decided.

"How's that friend of yours, Daisy?" she remembered to ask. "The girl from the farm. Is she any better?"

"It takes time, but her letters are much more cheerful now," Daisy said. "So what are you all doing lately? Have you heard from Baz again? And what of Elsie's wedding plans?"

To Immy, it was odd how detached she seemed from them all. How she was one step removed from her real family, and so firmly established in this one. Odd, and a little sad.

"Baz is fine. Elsie's still dithering, and I'm going to a dance with Helen and her parents soon," she said abruptly.

"Lovely," Daisy said carelessly, her enquiries done.

Later, Rose took her eldest niece aside.

"Don't take too much notice of Daisy's apparent lack of interest, Immy dear. She doesn't mean anything by it."

"I know. We've all moved on, though, haven't we? Ever since Mother – well, that changed everything, didn't it?"

It had torn the family apart in a way none of them had imagined, but it seemed too churlish to say as much to Aunt Rose, who had welcomed two of Frances's five children into her home out of love, with no thought of duty.

"You still have her memory, and nothing can change that, Imogen. And she'd be so proud to think you were going to wear her lovely dress at your dance."

She turned the conversation neatly, and all the way back to Bristol in the car – she now considered herself a competent driver – Immy thought what a diplomat Rose could be when she wanted to be. No wonder they all loved her.

By now she knew there was one more thing she had to do before she finally decided to wear her mother's dress. She needed to get Helen's opinion of it, knowing she would get an honest one. If Helen thought the dress was unsuitable, then she would have to think again – at the risk of breaking her father's heart.

–

"Helen, can you come here one evening?" Immy telephoned her as soon as she reached home again. "I need to show you my dance dress and see what you think."

"Oh, spiffing! I can be with you around seven o'clock tomorrow if you like. I'll bring along one or two of mine, and you can help me choose what I'm going to wear. We can have a trying-on session. It'll be fun."

Everything was fun to Helen, Immy thought, still smiling as she put down the phone. And of course Helen would have a selection to choose from…well, so had she, she admitted. Her father had offered her the choice of her mother's dresses. But she still thought the blue and silver was the one.

The following evening in Immy's bedroom, Helen gasped. Her eyes widened even more as Immy paraded in it.

"It's absolutely gorgeous, darling. It must have cost a fortune. But when did you get it made, for heaven's sake? You always say you don't go to many social occasions, but I'm beginning to doubt it. You are a dark horse, Immy!"

Immy burst out laughing, glowing at Helen's reaction, and ready to tease her a little longer.

"You don't think it looks a little dated, then?"

"It's right up to the minute and you know it. Come on now, where did you get it? I need the name of the designer."

"It's not new, though I think it was only worn a few times. It was my mother's. One of her stage dresses."

Helen sat back on the bed.

"Good Lord," she said at last. "I hardly know what to say. It's really beautiful, Immy, and I shall be as jealous as old Harry. You'll be the belle of the ball."

"Stop it, for heaven's sake. You're embarrassing me. I'm just so thankful my father offered me the choice of them."

"You mean there are more?" Helen almost squeaked.

"Lots."

"Then you have to get out more, Immy, if only to wear them. I shall take you in hand and see that you do."

Immy laughed. "Don't be silly. Elsie's going to be allowed to choose a special dress too, for when she and Joe go on their honeymoon. Mother had such lovely things."

"Well, if they're all like this he'll love her in it."

"So show me what you're going to wear," Immy said, suddenly remembering Elsie's tearful comment that it wasn't fair that even a honeymoon might have to be arranged according to the arrogant demands of Adolf Hitler.

"I think it will be the pink brocade," Helen announced. "Or perhaps the green. I'll try them both and you can tell me what you think."

Whichever one it was, they both knew it wasn't going to be a patch on the lovely fluid blue and silver gown that had once graced the stage and held the audience enthralled as it undulated to Frances Caldwell's exquisite dancing.

–

"We may bring the wedding forward," Elsie told her sister. "I don't know what Daddy will think, though I've got his written permission in advance. But Joe doesn't want to wait until October to enlist, and he wants us to be married before then."

"Elsie, you can't arrange it too near to the anniversary of Mother's death. I thought you had enough sense to wait until after that, at least. It would be far too emotional."

"I know all that! But life has to go on, doesn't it?"

Immy glowered at her. "How can you be so selfish and so thoughtless? Life ended for Daddy eleven months ago."

"No, it didn't, Immy, and if you only had eyes to see, you'd know he's already found some consolation."

Immy scoffed. "The Marys, you mean? Just because he spends a little time with them doesn't mean he's feeling amorous about them."

"Not them. Her. Mary Yard," Elsie stated, her voice clipped and resentful.

"I think you're imagining things. But would it be so very awful – after a decent few years, of course – if Father did think of marrying again?"

"I don't even want to think about it."

"Neither do I – but you obviously *have* been thinking about it, or you wouldn't have mentioned it," Immy pointed out. "What brought it up, anyway?"

"Joe and I were discussing how small a wedding we could have. But if we were to invite one or two friends, Daddy said maybe we could include the Marys."

"And that's it?"

"It was the way he said it, especially Mary Yard's name. I have a bad feeling about it, Immy."

Immy put her arm around her sister. "Well, you shouldn't have. I can't say I've thought about it seriously, but if Daddy wants to find a little happiness again, we shouldn't begrudge him the chance. And I can't think of anyone nicer than one of the Marys."

Though it would be different having her as a *stepmother*, of course… In unspoken agreement they changed the subject.

"Anyway," Immy said determinedly, "about your wedding. Whenever it is, you know Aunt Rose will insist on that new hat, don't you? And Daisy will expect to be a bridesmaid."

Elsie groaned. "It all gets a bit much, actually! I've been reading about all the fuss and planning that's involved in Mother's old etiquette book, and we really don't want to spend time on all that. We'd much rather keep it private, just the two of us. I wish I had the nerve to do what Baz did. Run away and leave a note, telling everyone we've tied the knot and we're staying in some little hotel, out of reach of everyone, blissfully happy just to be together and on our honeymoon. It's a far more romantic idea."

"You're not serious, I hope?"

"Of course not. Would I dare?"

She went off, laughing and blushing red, and Immy stared after her for a good few minutes.

Yes, sister dear, she thought, in answer to the airy question. *I do believe you would.*

—

Reading the morning newspaper over breakfast had become a necessary ritual for Quentin and his children, in addition to listening intently to the daily wireless bulletins.

"Though it's little more than a masochistic exercise these days," he told anyone who would listen, since all that the rags and the dour radio presenters' reports contained was bad news. This mid-August day was no exception.

"Good God. We're all going to have to carry identity cards now," Quentin exploded angrily, glowering at the newsprint. "What damned impertinence! We'll each be given a personal number, just as if we're pigs being sent to market. They may as well stamp it on our foreheads and be done with it."

"It's for security reasons, I suppose," Imogen said, knowing that with every new regulation imposed on them, the certainty of war came ever closer.

Quentin snorted. "Do they think there's any doubt about who's British and who isn't? You only have to look at us and listen to us."

His daughters tried not to smile at his indignation, knowing he was perfectly serious.

"I don't know about listening to us, Father. Not all of us talk the same. Joe's accent is very different from ours, for a start," Elsie pointed out.

"I'll grant you that, but we can understand it – just. It's not foreign – or Welsh."

Immy flinched. The mere mention of anything Welsh could instantly remind her of Morgan Raine.

"Welsh isn't foreign!" she said.

"I don't mean the boyos who work at Welsh Back market," Quentin went on. "But the national Welsh language might just as well be foreign for all anybody could understand it."

Little did he know that he had a daughter who had once been charmed by the lilting sound of it, and by the soft and seductive way Morgan had called her cariad and caressed her breasts, making her toes curl and her blood sing...

"What are you two mooning about now?" her father asked irritably. "Don't you have jobs to go to?"

"He's getting more upset as it gets closer to September," Elsie remarked to her sister as they went upstairs for their outdoor shoes. "I'm really sorry for you, Immy."

"Sorry for me? Why?" Startled, and still thinking about Morgan, she wondered for a ghastly moment if Elsie had heard any rumours about her liaison with the Welshman.

"Well, Mother dying a week after your birthday. You'll always remember it, won't you? But at least you can be thankful we didn't have the picnic on the day itself."

"And that's why you think Father's getting upset?"

"Of course. Well, and all this war talk doesn't help, naturally."

Immy's heartbeat slowed to normal again.

"Sometimes I think the talk's gone on so long that that's all it will ever be. Just talk."

"Tell that to Joe," Elsie said. "He doesn't think it's only talk for a minute. Nor do any of the girls at the shop. Some of them are talking about leaving Preston's and working in a munitions factory making aeroplane parts. Joe says Bristol won't be a safe place anymore, what with the docks and the aircraft industry here. He says—"

"Good Lord, Elsie, don't you have a single thought of your own? I'm sick of hearing what Joe says!"

"Well, pardon me. But at least he talks sense and doesn't go around with his head in the clouds thinking it's all a mirage. Helen's mother obviously thinks it's serious, with her fundraising schemes for servicemen. *And* her brother."

"All right, I'm sorry. The fact that I don't want to talk about it doesn't mean I don't think about it."

"There's no point in *not* talking about it, is there? It's not going to go away, Immy."

"Well, it's not here yet, and now I'm going to work," Immy said rudely, needing to get away from this newly serious-minded sister, who seemed to be showing far more political sense than she herself was.

She got out her bicycle and pedalled to her office in the city centre in a fury, noting as if for the first time just how many young men there were in uniform about the city now; how many older men were wearing the dark battledress of the ARP warden; how a general air of gloom and anxious activity seemed to have settled over what had been, until now, a mellow and lovely summer.

Kenneth Harris looked up and smiled as she entered the reception area of the office. His expression changed when he saw her flushed face and noted her prickly countenance.

"Good morning, Imogen," he said with the heartiness of bolstering her up. "You're looking a mite less cheerful than usual this morning. Nothing wrong, I hope."

He was as sweet as ever, as round as a butterball, and full of concern for her. He fussed over his clients' welfare, and he worried about her like a mother hen. But right now the attention was too much.

She burst into tears and rushed through to the back room where the tea-making things were stored. She thrust the kettle under the cold tap with shaking hands, just to busy herself.

Blindly, she felt him take the kettle from her, then put his hands firmly on her shoulders.

"My dear girl, what have I said?"

"Nothing, Mr Harris. It's not you. It's me. It's the news. It's *everything*."

"My goodness," he said in bewilderment, not really understanding such passion at nine o'clock on a Monday morning. "The last thing I heard, you were practically floating on air because you were going to a dance with that nice friend of yours. Has it all fallen through?"

She gave a tremulous smile. She knew he loved hearing about her family and took a vicarious interest in all their doings. He led such a small, narrow life compared with hers.

In fact, she thought shamefacedly, it was far narrower than hers. She had a family who loved her; he had no one and lived in a small cottage with only a cat for company. She was lucky compared to him.

"No, it hasn't fallen through. I'm just having a few bad moments. It's because the anniversary of my mother's death is coming nearer. Sometimes the awfulness of that day comes over me again."

"Of course it does. I still remember when my own dear mother died. You never really get over it, especially if you were as close as fleas on a dog's back... That's better," he went on, as she gave a watery smile at his tasteless simile. "Now then, you go and dry your eyes, and I'll make us some tea."

"It's really me who should be doing it," she mumbled.

"Nonsense, dear. I've been making tea for years."

Chapter Seventeen

"God Almighty, so the prodigal's returned," Quentin said, opening the door to the virtual stranger standing there.

The thought was in his head before any other, because even in that first startled instant he could see how his son had broadened and matured in these few short weeks. He had gone away a boy and come home a man.

His natural anger surged up at the memory of Baz's leaving note. A son was still a son for all that, and answerable to his father.

"I suppose you expect me to welcome you back, do you?"

"I hope so, Father," Baz said, refusing to be intimidated in the way he had once been, though his heart banged uncomfortably in his chest in a less than manly way. He held on to the fact that as far as physical endurance went, he'd had more perilous encounters in those few weeks than his father had ever had. And come out of it triumphant. Wanting more. Eager for more.

He looked at his father unsmilingly, making no attempt to step inside the house until he was invited, still defensive.

"I'm sorry for the way I left, Father, but it's all I ever wanted, even if the sea gets a bit rough at times."

At such an understatement, a muscle at the corner of his mouth twitched, and without warning his lips went with it. He was suddenly vulnerable, wanting approval, wanting his father to say everything was all right and not to condemn him. They both knew it.

"You'd best come inside and tell me about it, then," Quentin said gruffly. He held the door wide, and the next minute his son was clasped in his arms.

Just as quickly they broke apart in hot embarrassment, but not before Quentin had felt the thickness in his throat, and Baz had dashed away the shine of tears.

Then Imogen came rushing out of the sitting-room and hugged him tight, and the moment was gone.

"You little wretch, have you any idea what you've put us all through?" she burst out. She was too full of gladness to see him safe to be cross for long, however. "You shouldn't have done it, Baz, but I must say you look well."

"I am well," he said, wriggling away from her. "Why wouldn't I be, when they call me the ship's mascot now?"

"Good God, they must be desperate if they put their faith in a ferry-lad for a mascot. Father Neptune must be squirming in his watery grave," Quentin said with heavy humour, his sarcasm tempered by a stronger feeling that all was right in his domestic world, if not outside his front door.

Immy laughed. "He's not such a boy now, is he? I swear you've grown two inches already, Baz."

He grinned with pleasure, discovering to his surprise that it was good to go away and come home again. It made them look at one another differently. Respect one another differently. Yes, it felt good.

"Where's Elsie?" he said next.

"Out with Joe, as usual," Immy told him.

"Are they married yet?"

"Hey now, boy," Quentin said, "you've only been away a few weeks, not an eternity. There's time enough for Elsie to be thinking about marriage."

"What about you, Immy?" He looked at her with mischief in his eyes, telling her that he knew far too much about her and Morgan for comfort. "Don't tell me you're letting our Elsie leave you behind."

"That's enough of that talk," his father said, reminding him that he was still an adolescent. "Besides, not every young woman wants to be married, especially in such troubled times."

"I do eventually, Father," Immy said indignantly, in case he should think otherwise. But she wouldn't spoil Baz's homecoming by getting upset because he had unintentionally made her feel the spinster sister.

Baz didn't stay very long. He was glad to have made his peace, but he was eager to see Enoch Bray and get his head down there for a night or two until the crew were off on the next trip. But he promised to visit them all again soon.

"Make sure that you do. This is always your home, Baz," his father reminded him.

Elsie was annoyed that she'd missed her brother, but she and Joe had had far more important things to discuss. Private things that concerned no one else but themselves – for the time being, anyway.

She was tempted to confide in Immy, but some secrets weren't for sharing with a third person, however much you loved them. There'd be time enough for that later. In any case, Immy was getting too het up about this dance in Bath and staying in hotel for a night.

What a narrow world they all inhabited! As if it was the end of the world to be sleeping in a strange bed for one night. Her darling Joe would be going away to heaven knew where soon, sleeping in tents or camps wherever the army sent him. She didn't care to question him too closely.

Elsie shivered, not understanding the madness of men. For months now, if not longer, there had been talk of war. If it was so imminent and so inevitable, why didn't they just get on with it, instead of planning their strategies and marshalling their troops and building up supplies of evil weapons as if they were pushing toy soldiers around a make-believe battleground or playing with men like marionettes on a string? Why not just begin?

The sooner it began, the sooner it would end, and all this nonsense of putting up black-out curtains at the windows of their houses so that no chink of light would show through to warn an unseen enemy would be over. All the evacuee children separated from their mothers could go back where they belonged, and people wouldn't have to carry those nasty little cardboard boxes containing gas masks around with them all the time. There would be no need for her father's despised identity cards to be issued.

She had said all this to Joe in an impassioned voice, proud of using the kind of logic that was usually attributed to Imogen. And alone in his room at his digs, where the landlady turned a blind eye since they were a betrothed couple, he had kissed her lips and her eyes with tenderness and spoken to her gently.

"Darling Elsie, don't you know that the government is desperate to do everything in its power to ward off the evil day for as long as possible, and is doing its best to keep the peace negotiations with Hitler alive?"

"But it won't work, will it?" she said, angry at his patronising attitude. "Hitler's riding roughshod over everything in his way. He won't rest until he conquers the world."

"That's why he has to be stopped, one way or another. We'll go down fighting before we see him conquer Britain, but only when the last hope of peace has gone. But I'm glad you're taking it seriously."

"Please don't treat me like a child, Joe! Of course I'm taking it seriously. I just want to get it over with, so we can all get back to normal. Do you think I'm eager for you to go to war? Do you think I want to send you away to be killed?"

Her eyes brimmed with unshed tears as the horror of it engulfed her, and with a smothered oath he folded her in his arms and held her very tight.

"I don't plan on being killed when I'll have you to come home to. I'm planning for our future, Elsie, for my wife and my children, and if this monster has to be stopped before that's possible, then so be it."

"I'm sorry. You make me ashamed," she whispered.

"Don't be. Just remember we have a future to share. Meanwhile, let's make the most of the present."

He put the words into action very satisfactorily, and for a blissful hour they forgot everything about wars and partings and cherished the time they had together.

—

As the day of the fund-raising dance in Bath grew nearer, Imogen did her best to forget all talk of war as well, though it was almost an impossibility now. Talk of it was on everybody's lips, and the entire city seemed to vibrate with anxiety and fear. Children were being sent out of Bristol to the country on extended visits to relatives, and everyone knew it was in expectation of the announcement.

By now Quentin was constantly tuning in the wireless for news reports and cursing under his breath whenever the battery ran out without warning, and someone had to rush along to the motoring garage to get it recharged.

Immy shared her sister's feelings. Why didn't they just get on with it so that everyone knew what they were doing? All this indecision was setting everyone's nerves on edge.

Even Kenneth Harris, normally so cheerful and almost childishly boisterous, was saying gloomily at the end of a quiet day that he didn't suppose many folk would want to be buying or renting houses until they knew what was what.

"People will always need somewhere to live, Mr Harris," Immy pointed out. "People will still get married and need a home of their own. Others will have more children and need larger homes, or they'll move to Bristol from other towns for the industrial work. I'm sure we needn't worry too much."

For once, he looked at her as if she didn't know what she was talking about, and without his usual tolerance.

"That's very short-sighted of you, if I might say so, Imogen. Who do you think will want to move to a city that's likely to be a prime target for German air raids?"

"Well, Preston's Emporium did, for a start."

She defended them, which was ironic in the extreme, since Preston's plan to open in Bristol was the start of a chain reaction resulting in her father losing his business.

It hadn't really turned out so badly, she admitted. Baz had got his way. Daisy had forgotten her one-time dream of going on the stage and seemed remarkably set on a nursing career. Teddy adored his life with Aunt Rose and Uncle Bertie. Elsie had found happiness with Joe.

And she *liked* secretarial work, she found herself thinking, almost in surprise. Perhaps she hadn't been destined to be a shopkeeper. She would probably never have learned to drive a car, either, if things had stayed the same. Things had a habit of turning out for the best – usually.

"I'm thinking of closing down," Kenneth Harris said gently, gauging her reaction as he did so.

"What did you say?" she gasped, wondering if she could possibly have heard him properly.

"Think about it, Imogen. We've done hardly any business lately. You know that as well as I do. Look how quiet we've been this past week. It's only been the two of us catching up on the administrative work. It's no way to run a business, and much as I love your company, my dear, I'm not sure I can really afford you if things continue this way."

Her heart was beating so fast she felt sick.

"But I don't want to leave," she stammered. "I don't want you to close down. What will you do?" She just managed not to say, "What will *I* do?"

"What everyone else is doing. Decamp to the country. I have a married brother in Cornwall who runs a market garden. He's been asking me to go in with him for ages, and I think I shall probably do so."

"I see. It's all cut and dried, then?" She tried not to feel that he was throwing her to the wolves without a second thought.

The next moment she knew how wrong she was. He caught both her hands in his, his face as red as fire.

"Not quite. Why don't you come with me, Imogen?"

"What do you mean?" she said, her heart thudding even faster now. At this rate she'd expire soon – and then her future would be settled without any problem, she thought.

She suppressed a hysterical desire to laugh, since she realised he was being deadly serious. Excruciatingly so.

"I know I'm not the most demonstrative of men, nor the most handsome. I've never considered marriage before, but you and I have always been comfortable together, haven't we?"

She felt as if she was being strangled as his clammy hands tightened over hers. She struggled to free herself.

"Mr Harris, forgive me if I'm misunderstanding you," she croaked, knowing darned well that she was not. "I do hope you're not proposing to me. If you are, then I'm afraid it's out of the question."

He stepped back a pace, his face as crumpled as an old newspaper now. He spoke with clumsy embarrassment.

"Of course it is. I can't think what possessed me to make such a suggestion, and I beg you to forget it ever happened."

"I will – but I won't forget the honour you do me, Mr Harris, and I don't mean to hurt your feelings."

"You haven't. No, indeed." He was almost fervent now. "As I said, I have never considered myself a marrying man before, and it was a moment of madness on my part. No, far better to go on as we are for the time being."

"But how long will that be?" Immy said.

"One more week," he said decisively. "I plan to close at the end of next week and move to Cornwall."

Whether or not this decision was so final because of her rejection, Immy didn't know. In those startled seconds she was alternately thankful she wouldn't have the embarrassment of working with him for much longer in the circumstances – and appalled that she was so soon going to be unemployed.

But to wed a man whose one reason for wanting her to marry him was that they had always been *comfortable* together? It wasn't the way she wanted to think about marriage. Her parents' relationship had been a loving and joyful one, until Frances's cruel illness had changed everything. She was sure it had been completely fulfilled, and right until the end, the love had been there. Even Aunt Rose and Uncle Bertie, for all their frequent spats, couldn't hide their love for each other. That was the way they expressed it.

Elsie and Joe too…she didn't need an interpreter to give her the reason for Elsie's glowing cheeks whenever she came home from seeing Joe. That was what love was like, and what it should be like. That passion, and that feeling that you couldn't exist without the other person, that you were only half alive when they weren't there. It certainly wasn't enough to be merely *comfortable* with one another.

"I think it's time I went home, don't you?" she said abruptly, suddenly feeling sad for a man who had obviously never known the meaning of passion, and didn't seem likely to do so. But she wasn't sorry enough to marry him.

"Another day tomorrow, then," he said, as he always did. "See you in the morning?"

He looked at her desperately, as if afraid she was going to tell him he could rot in Hades. Either that, or he was scared that she was about to spill his ridiculous proposal to the entire world.

"Of course. There's going to be a lot to tidy up in a week, isn't there? At least that will keep us busy."

She was rewarded by seeing a huge flicker of relief on his face. And no, she thought, cycling home, he had never been the marrying kind, and she doubted that he ever would be.

"You are joking, aren't you?" Helen said with a hoot of laughter. They were driving to Bath in Helen's car, since her parents had gone ahead earlier. "He didn't actually expect you to marry him?"

"You promised not to say a word about this, Helen," Immy said crossly. "I was shocked at first, but then I felt quite sorry for him."

"But what did he actually *say*? Did he go down on one knee and profess his undying love?" Helen giggled, in her element now, trying to imagine Kenneth Harris's struggle to get down on the floor at all.

"Of course not. Hardly! He said we'd always been comfortable together."

"Good God. Well, if that's a not a passion killer, I don't know what is," Helen said scornfully. "You deserve far more than that, darling."

"I know. I *want* more than that. I'd never settle for less, either. If anything, his sad proposal has made me realise it, Helen. I'll never settle for second best."

"Good for you. I suppose that's why those Marys of yours have never married again. Once you've tasted champagne, why settle for beer? Mind you, they've been a long time without, haven't they? Maybe they've forgotten how."

Immy didn't follow her meaning for a moment, and then she laughed. "You've got a saucy mind, Helen Church!"

"No, I haven't, just a normal one. It has to be more than twenty years since they were widowed."

"They probably never even think about it anymore."

"Why not? Do you suppose all the urges stop when you reach forty – or even fifty?"

"I don't know!"

"Well, neither do I," Helen admitted, "but it seems a great waste of married life if they do."

"Can we please get off this subject?" Immy said, her thoughts reverting to her father, who was not yet fifty, and spent considerable time with the Marys nowadays. She certainly didn't want to think of him having urges. But she grinned to herself. It was impossible, of course.

"What now?" Helen said.

"Nothing."

"Oh well, I suppose you'll tell me when you're ready. How are the great lovers, by the way? Elsie and Joe?"

"Blooming, of course, as you would expect."

"I wonder if they've done it yet," Helen said thoughtfully.

"*Helen!*"

Helen laughed, since the response was exactly what she had expected. Considering Immy had had a pretty torrid affair with that Welsh fellow, by all accounts, she was extraordinarily reticent about her sister's romance. Still, she couldn't fault Immy's loyalty.

"By the way, did I tell you James will be at the dance tonight?" she said casually. "He got home late last night on a measly thirty-six-hour pass. He'll be joining us at the hotel later, so at least we'll have one partner to share."

"How lovely," was all Immy said.

What she was remembering was the way his hands had gently raked through her tangled hair, and the sweet way he had dried it for her. She was remembering that moment when she was sure she had felt the warmth of his lips on the nape of her neck, and his words in response to her own.

"I'll be dreaming of sweeter things," she had said.

"And so will I," he had replied softly.

She shivered as the car rattled over the bumps in the road. They were nearing the glorious city of Bath with its elegant buildings and beautiful abbey. What an insult it had been for a man of forty years old to half-heartedly propose marriage to her because they had always been comfortable together!

She would feel quite differently about a proposal from a man of her own age. A virile, dynamic young man with heroic ideals and film-star looks. Even though she had known him as a friend for so long, she experienced a sudden yearning in her soul to feel those same hands in her hair once more, to feel the touch of his lips on her neck – and in other places – just to reassure her that she was a desirable young woman and could stir a man's senses. And she was very much aware that it was a dangerous game to play.

"Here we are, Immy," Helen said, breaking into her turbulent thoughts.

She realised they had drawn up outside a very large and impressive hotel with flags flying over the portals. A uniformed doorman appeared at once to open the car doors and give them a smart salute. Immy had never been in such a splendid place before, and she felt momentarily overawed.

"Imagine them in their flannel underwear, darling," Helen whispered. "That will always bring them down to size."

She turned to the porters coming out of the hotel foyer now and gave them a dazzling smile.

"The bags are in the boot for Miss Church and Miss Caldwell's room," she told them.

Immy was impressed by such cool confidence, but then, Helen was well used to this. Well, if she didn't want to look as if she had hayseeds in her teeth, she decided she had better appear used to it too.

The room was what Kenneth Harris would call very well appointed. It was deeply carpeted, with twin beds covered in deep red brocaded eiderdowns and solid oak furniture that had been lovingly polished. There was even an adjacent bathroom.

"Gosh," was all Immy could say, when she had inspected everything minutely.

"Put your eyes back in their sockets, darling, and pretend you're used to it," Helen advised, reminding her of her own conclusion. "That's the way to get by. You don't think my family lives in such grand surroundings every day, do you? In fact, you know we don't! But if you want to be treated like rich folk, you have to act like them. That's the secret. Let's unpack quickly and then go downstairs and hobnob with anyone we can find who looks interesting."

The bags had arrived in the room before they had, and they quickly hung their evening gowns in the wardrobe and despatched everything else to the dressing-table drawers.

"Ready for the fray?" Helen said.

"Quite ready," said Immy.

She wasn't really, but without warning one of her mother's sayings came into her head.

"Hold your head up high and let them see you think you're worth a king's ransom, my darling. If you think it, so will everyone else."

It echoed Helen's reasoning. Immy gave a wistful little smile, murmured a silent thank you to Frances, and lifted her head and swept out of the room behind Helen as if she had been born to high society.

Helen's parents greeted them both warmly, thankful that their daughter had got there safely.

"More safely than if I'd been driving, Mrs Church," Immy said smilingly.

"Nonsense, Imogen. You're becoming quite an expert, going all the way to Weston-super-Mare to visit your relatives."

"Mother still doesn't think it quite ladylike to drive a motor car, though," Helen said teasingly.

"It just wasn't done much in my day, dear – save when we were required to drive ambulances and suchlike in the war, of course, but those were exceptional circumstances."

"And very likely to come again," Helen said, as her mother drifted off to greet more acquaintances.

"She's really in her element, isn't she?" Immy said, seeing the ease with which she greeted all comers.

"Oh, Mother's a whiz at organising. If she had her way she'd organise Hitler too. She'd have no truck with all this shilly-shallying."

"Let's forget it for now," Immy said swiftly. "We're here to enjoy ourselves, remember?"

"Of course. Laugh and be merry, for tomorrow we—"

"Tomorrow we'll probably all have aching heads and even worse feet," Immy forestalled her. "Do they serve afternoon tea here, Helen? I'm parched after holding on to my hat and my nerves with worry about your driving."

They went into the tea lounge with linked arms, still teasing one another. Watching them, Helen's mother thought what a superb example of graceful young womanhood they were. Helen with her blonde curls framing her pretty face and her typically English blue eyes, and her beautiful friend with delicate features and that glorious red hair falling in natural waves to her shoulders.

She turned with a sigh as someone claimed her, and at once became her efficient self again, with no time to waste on nostalgic reminiscences of a time when she too had been young and brimming with health and vitality of a different kind.

They were to have an early dinner in the hotel dining-room, and then dress for the dance which officially began at eight o'clock.

"There's no point in getting there on time, though," Helen said, with prior knowledge of such events. "People drift in at least half an hour late, and we don't want to stick out like sore thumbs, or even worse, look like wallflowers. We don't want to seem too eager to catch a man, either."

"I presume you mean to dance with?" Immy said, with a smile in her voice.

"Oh, of course! What else could I mean?"

"And what's the name of this committee man you were so interested in?" Immy continued archly.

"Paul. Paul Stevens."

Helen said it too quickly for it not to have been on her mind, and she blushed.

"Oh, all right, I admit I'm keen to see him again. I only met him once, but he was quite charming."

"And he's probably got a wife and ten children at home."

Helen's face was a picture of dismay. "Good Lord, do you know, that never occurred to me. But you may be right. Not that he'd have *ten*. He's hardly old enough for that. He must be nearer thirty than twenty, though."

"Oh, *old*," Immy said, hearing the almost imperceptible loss of interest in Helen's voice. She knew her friend too well. Until she was really, properly, madly in love, she was quite happy to flirt harmlessly. And just as ready to flit from one possible to the next.

It made her sound shallow and fast, when in reality, Immy knew she was not. The traumatic experience with Robert Preston had told her that. Helen was just waiting for the right man, that was all. The same as Immy was.

When they had fastened each other's evening gowns, brushed their hair to a sheen, applied as much face make-up as was decent and doused themselves in their favourite scent, they turned and assessed each other, and then looked at their dual reflections in the long mirror.

"Wow!" they said simultaneously, and then laughed at their own vanity.

"We're so modest, aren't we?" Immy giggled. "But I do think we look rather spiffing, Helen, don't you?"

"I think we shall make quite an entrance," Helen agreed. "Shall we do just that?"

Immy still had to make an effort to hide her nervousness. She had never been to a function like this, and when they reached the ballroom, festooned with balloons and Union flags, the glitter of it all nearly took her breath away.

The orchestra was playing a waltz tune, and a dozen couples had already taken to the floor while others chatted amicably as they greeted old friends.

"You see? Hardly anyone's here yet, except Mother's committee and a few others," Helen whispered. "And him."

"Who?" But she already knew who it would be. She could tell by the coolness in Helen's voice that the male half of the couple her eyes were following must be Paul Stevens. She also guessed that the rather prim-looking lady holding his arm was almost certainly his wife. So much for romance.

"Oh well," she began.

"Oh well," Helen agreed, cutting her off. "Never mind, there are plenty more fish in the sea, as they say. And Mother always insists that people *mingle* at these affairs, so that's what we shall do. Lovely word, isn't it?"

Immy admired her poise. Helen would never get entangled with a married man, or one who was promised to someone else. No more would she herself. She couldn't imagine anything worse than having to share a lover. She had discovered that awful feeling for herself when she had seen Morgan Raine with his arm around another girl.

She brushed off the memory. It was over. In the past. She was here to enjoy herself, and to forget all of that.

Many more people were coming into the ballroom now. It was a thrill just to see the dazzling jewels the ladies were wearing, and how rich and important they looked. Mrs Church would surely do well with her fund-raising for servicemen's comforts tonight, Immy found herself thinking.

Eventually it began to be almost too crowded for comfort. There was a roll on the drums and the MC took his place on the platform, clearing his throat.

"Ladies and gentlemen, I've no intention of holding up your enjoyment for more than a few moments," he said, to the accompaniment of a few polite cheers, "but there are one or two formalities I can't ignore.

"The first is to thank Mrs Church, our indefatigable hostess, and her committee, for arranging this gathering tonight." He waited for further cheers to die down. "The second is to remind you why we're here. As well as to enjoy ourselves, we want to raise as much money as possible for our gallant servicemen, so when the raffle tickets come around, please dig deeply into your pockets to stand a chance of winning one of the valuable prizes to be awarded at the end of the evening.

"And I've one last request. Whatever tomorrow may bring, we've pledged not to make a single mention of war this evening. We're here to have fun, and that's what we want you all to do, in the best possible way we know."

He was almost deafened by the roars of approval. The drum rolls continued until he had left the stage and the orchestra began playing again. From then on, everyone took to the dance floor, and did exactly as they had been told.

Immy and Helen had no lack of partners. At one point, Immy lost sight of her friend. She was taking a short breather after the exuberant whirling of her most recent, perspiring escort. Right now she was more than happy to watch the more energetic dancers jigging frantically to the Gay Gordons for a few moments while she caught her breath.

When it ended, the lights dimmed, and the dance floor cleared before the slower strains of a dreamy waltz tune coaxed the romantics back again.

"May I have this dance?" she heard a deep, masculine voice say right behind her.

A voice she knew, and one that made her heart leap. She turned around quickly.

"You look simply stunning, and you take my breath away," James said quietly, the moment before she went into his arms.

Chapter Eighteen

Imogen couldn't have pinpointed the exact moment she realised she was falling in love with James Church. She couldn't even decide if it was love that she was feeling.

It could just have been the effects of the magical evening, which had seemed headier and more vibrant than usual, perhaps because of everyone's determination to follow the MC's instructions and give no thought to an impending war.

Whatever it was, Immy felt happier than she had at any time since breaking up with Morgan. James became her sole escort for the evening, and when she asked him laughingly if he wasn't expected to ask some other young ladies to dance, he shook his head decisively.

"Why should I, when I'm already dancing with the girl of my dreams?" he whispered seductively in her ear, his arm tightening around her waist for yet another slow waltz.

"I just thought your mother might think you had a duty to do so," she murmured, too much on fire to question whether his words were just a tease.

"Not at all. I'm not one of Mother's committee sheep. I don't conform, Immy. I never have. I thought you knew that. I could never follow in my father's footsteps and be a lawyer."

"Is that why you joined the tank regiment? Is there some special kind of excitement in that?"

He looked down into her face, his voice definitely teasing now. "You have to pay a penalty for that remark."

"What do you mean?" she said, her heartbeat quickening.

"Our glorious MC declared that there was to be no hint of war tonight, and you've just broken the rule by mentioning my regiment," he said solemnly.

"I have not!" Immy protested. "I think you're stretching the rule a little, James!"

He shook his head. "I insist that you take the punishment."

"Oh dear. Should I start quaking in my shoes?"

"You may well do so! Such penalties cannot be paid in public. We have to go outside on the terrace to spare your blushes."

He took her hand and began weaving his way through the dancers, so that she had no choice but to follow him. It was all delicious nonsense, but the ballroom *was* becoming unbearably hot and stuffy now, and a breath of fresh air on the wide terrace adjoining it would be very welcome.

He led her across the marbled floor, and they leaned over the edge of a secluded corner of the terrace, breathing in the scented air from the gardens below. By now the shadows had deepened and the night was a soft indigo, peppered with stars and lit by the crescent of the new moon. It was a night made for romance, for secret whisperings and vowed intentions.

Far below them the winding river Avon meandered through the city, glittering in the moonlight and reminding Immy for one heartbreaking moment of the way it had looked on that fateful day when her mother had spiralled to her death from Clifton Downs. But she blinked the image away, not wanting to spoil these perfect moments with such anguished thoughts. Frances would never have wanted that.

James was now turning her to face him, his hands gentle on her slender shoulders. She could feel the heat of his fingers softly caressing the skin at the nape of her neck, making her shiver – but not with cold. Never with cold, when there was fire raging inside her. And she was instantly certain she had not imagined that other time. None of it.

He still said nothing, but her nerve ends were tingling with sweet anticipation now. Her mouth opened in a tremulous smile as she looked up into his face.

"Well, James?" she said.

And though she could hardly bear to play the waiting game any longer, her words were slow and long drawn out, as if something inside her wanted to hold on to this moment forever. She was sure that whatever had been between them all the time she had known him was about to be changed forever.

"Well, my lovely Imogen," he said softly. "Are you ready to pay your penalty?"

"I believe so," she whispered, knowing what it would be. His arms went around her, and she melted against him, raising her face for his kiss.

The first kiss between them had all the passion of lovers. It was a kiss that was deep and possessive, parting her lips so that she could taste the freshness of his mouth and feel the sharpness of his teeth against her tongue. A kiss that stirred her soul as she wound her arms about his neck and held him close, so close that she could feel every sinewy part of him and revelled in it. A kiss that reminded her that she knew what it was to feel unrestrained passion, and to have a man wanting her. And there was no doubt in her mind now that James wanted her.

They broke away after a few minutes in order to breathe. They remained close, still locked in one another's arms, their mouths still no more than a breath apart, their hearts pounding in a mutual dance of desire.

"For the first time, I regret having to rejoin my regiment so soon," he said huskily. "And now I've broken the rule. You'll have to extract a penalty from me, my love."

"If I must," Imogen said, feeling a delicious sense of fun at his banter. For of course he knew what he was saying and doing, just as she did. The kissing went on…and on…and needed no more encouragement of rule-breaking to make them fully aware of the significance of this night.

–

"Where on earth did you get to? I lost sight of you hours ago," Helen complained, when at last she came to bed in the early hours of the morning, having danced until her feet throbbed.

By then, Immy was lying in bed, gazing up at the ceiling and realising how much truth there was in the old saying that love was blind. It had to be, if you could know a person for so long, and yet not really know him at all. Until now…

"Immy? Why haven't you put the light on?" Helen asked, switching on a bedside lamp and making Immy flinch. "Or were you asleep? Oh God, I'm so thoughtless."

"I wasn't asleep. I was thinking. Dreaming."

"You must have had a good time, then. So did I. I met the most marvellous man, and Paul Stevens can go and—"

She suddenly realised that Immy wasn't listening to her ramblings. She sat down on her own bed in her petticoat, her lovely evening gown tossed carelessly on the floor, and stared at her friend.

"Who was it, Immy? You must tell! I've never seen you look so moonstruck before – well, not since MR."

"Don't even mention him. He's in the past."

"*And?*" Helen almost squeaked. "Who's going to be the future? The last time I caught sight of you, you were dancing with James and grinning up at him like a Cheshire cat."

"Was I?"

Immy felt her mouth curve at the memory of James smiling down at her, of her heart doing somersaults, and of the dawning emotions between them. Although if Helen was to be believed, James had harboured feelings for her for quite a while. And she was quite ready to believe it.

"*Immy!*" Helen breathed. "Am I reading the signs right? You and James – at last? So I was right all along in saying you would make the perfect couple!"

Immy gave a small laugh. "Hold your horses! We only had a few dances, that was all. And a breather on the terrace. And the rest is none of your business," she added teasingly.

But her flushed face and luminous eyes said far more than words, and for once, Helen took the hint and left her to her private dreams.

"Tell me tomorrow," she said, turning away from such blatant happiness. She finished undressing and turned out the lamp before climbing into bed and falling asleep instantly.

It was more than Imogen could do. She was still hearing the sound of James's rich voice in her head, feeling his arms around her waist, his hands gentle on her shoulders and elsewhere, his mouth on hers as the silly excuses for paying penalties faded out of existence.

Because they had known one another for so long, and had already discussed every topic beneath the sun, there was no need for the conventional explorations between tentative new lovers as they talked long into the night.

"Will you write to me?" he asked.

"As often as you want me to."

"All the time. And I promise to write back. I'll need to know that you're thinking of me and missing me."

"You won't need my letters for that, James. Just keep the certainty in your heart."

It seemed the most natural thing in the world, on a night that was charged with tension, to be speaking so frankly. A beautiful summer's night, yet they all felt the threat hanging over them like a dark shadow. And with it the fear that the peace and tranquillity that was prevalent in their corner of England was so soon to be shattered.

"When I can't actually hear your voice your letters will mean a great deal to me," James said, interspersing each word with a kiss. "So promise me you'll write."

"Of course I promise."

He hesitated. "I won't ask for more right now, Imogen, but I'd like to think of you as my young lady. My special girl. What do you say?"

"I say that I can think of nothing I want more than to be your special girl, James," she said softly, her reply as solemn as a vow.

As she remembered those words her eyes were damp. He might not have asked for more, and maybe it was not the best of times to be looking ahead to personal happiness. But if you didn't look ahead and plan for the future, you might as well admit defeat.

And even though the words hadn't been said, Imogen sensed that there was already a very special unspoken promise between them. She finally drifted into sleep, content.

–

"So are you and James going steady now?" Helen demanded the next morning.

Imogen awoke with an enormous headache stabbing her behind the eyes and the sinking feeling that the previous night might all have been a dream. Had James Church really said those seductive things to her, kissed her so passionately, and made her promise to write to him as often as possible?

"I shouldn't think so," she said crossly. "One swallow doesn't make a summer, does it?"

"What the dickens do birds have to do with it? I hope you're not going to go all coy on me, Immy. You know I'm dying to hear everything."

"There's nothing to tell. James and I danced a lot, we had some laughs, and we both probably drank a little too much champagne. That's all."

"And I suppose you've no intention of telling me anymore," Helen stated.

"Absolutely right. So don't ask."

"You're a selfish pig sometimes, Immy, but I still love you," Helen said cheerfully. "Anyway, if you won't tell me what went on, I won't tell you about Adam."

Immy sat up in bed, her red hair tumbling about her shoulders as she heard the dreamy note in her friend's voice.

"Adam?"

She knew Helen well enough to know she wouldn't be able to keep it to herself for long.

"He's Paul Stevens's brother — you know, the committee man I told you about. You were right about Paul, by the way. He's married with children – but Adam isn't. He's in the navy and he's adorable. So it seems we were both lucky last night."

She was blatantly fishing again, but Immy simply laughed and leaped out of bed, suddenly infected by Helen's enthusiasm. Remaining in this room a moment longer, when she could be downstairs in the dining-room having breakfast with James, seemed like a total waste of time.

The thought of sharing breakfast with him in a hotel also sounded delightfully decadent and intimate, even if it would be in the company of James's family.

"I'm first in the bathroom," she called out gaily. Helen was still yawning lazily.

"Goodness, you working folk depress me," she grumbled.

By then, Immy was picking up the envelope that had been pushed under the bedroom door. It was addressed to her, and she didn't recognise the handwriting. She opened it quickly. It was from James.

> *Immy darling, this is the most awful luck, but my leave's up and I can't even see you this morning. We're almost certainly on the move, though God knows where. My guess is France, though I probably shouldn't say as much. I'll write as soon as I can. Meanwhile, keep the memory of our lovely evening in your heart as I will in mine. My love, James.*

She was numb, staring at the letter and hardly taking in the words, just the fact that he was gone. They had been on the brink of something wonderful, and it had already been snatched away from them. She knew what "being on the move" meant – and now she also knew what it meant for one's blood to run cold, as they said in all the thriller novels. It was as if an icy wind was blowing through this luxurious room.

"Immy, what's up?" she heard Helen say. The next minute she felt the letter being taken from her hands.

"Oh, what rotten luck," James's sister said. "I said it was a measly leave, didn't I? Never mind—" She paused, seeing Immy's white face. "My God, you *do* mind, don't you? Did something happen between you two last night?"

"Not really. Just that I think we fell in love. Isn't that a crazy thing to do when a war is about to happen?"

She felt her throat closing up as all the implications of it washed over her, and she rushed to the bathroom, closed the door and leaned against it, her heart thudding.

Stories of the last war were still vivid in many people's minds, recounted over and over again. People like the Marys had lost young husbands. Mothers had lost sons. Children had lost fathers. The repercussions of war were endless.

She had envied her sisters recently for their romantic attachments. But she hadn't really thought it through properly. Because as soon as Adolf Hitler and Prime Minister Chamberlain decided there could be no avoidance of the inevitable, then all of them were going to be parted.

Elsie's Joe was about to enlist…Daisy's young man was already an air cadet and learning to fly…last night Helen had met someone called Adam who was in the navy and would be doing his bit…and she and James Church had fallen in love and promised to write to one another. And wherever he was sent, he was going to drive a tank, which everybody knew was a very dangerous thing to do.

The heady euphoria of last night had already faded. Daylight made you see things differently, and what Immy saw was that it was a terrible waste of emotion to fall in love at all, when some madman was threatening to wipe out all the young men who were patriotic enough to fight for their country.

Would you have him be a conscientious objector? the treacherous little voice said inside her head. Of course she would not! She just wanted him safe, and here.

"Are you all right, Immy?" she heard Helen call out. "You aren't going to be all day in there, are you? I thought we'd take a walk around the city before we leave, unless you're anxious to get back to Bristol. I don't mind either way."

"I think I'd rather go home," Immy said in a choked voice. "If you're sure you don't mind."

It wasn't just that she couldn't bear to stay in a city that held such sweet memories for her. It was more a sense of urgency that made her want to be at home, inside the four familiar walls in the house where she had been born, surrounded by her family's love.

The sense of fear in her heart made her feel as vulnerable as a child, when just hours before she had never felt so much like a woman.

—

Aunt Rose was at pains to keep all news of impending war away from the three small boys in her care. Daisy didn't spend too much time reading the newspapers or listening to the wireless, preferring to maintain an ostrich-like approach to the whole thing. If she didn't see or hear too much about it, then it wasn't going to happen.

She still spent a little time at the Luckwell farm, exercising Lucy's horse and taking her own out for a trot. But she felt a little uncomfortable going there lately. Lucy's mother usually had such a red, blotchy face now. The recent news about Lucy wasn't good. Her state of health had suddenly deteriorated, she hardly ever wrote letters anymore, and Daisy couldn't bear to hear the latest reports. She also felt guilty that her own robust looks must sharpen the difference between herself and Lucy.

For the first time in her life Daisy had to face the real possibility that a friend of her own age might die.

Working at the hospital made things seem worse. By now Daisy knew what happened to people when they died. She knew the gruesome things nurses had to put up with. The awful smell that came from a patient who was dying. The disgusting messes one had to clear up. And after death, plugging the orifices, as they called it, and the tasteful laying out, so that grieving loved ones could view the deceased as calmly as possible.

Many bereaved folk said how lovely and peaceful the deceased looked. To Daisy, they simply looked dead. Grey and dead. It was the one thing in her nursing work she hated, and the one thing she knew she had to accept if she didn't want to give it all up. And she had no intention of doing that. Even if her friend died – and every time she thought of the possibility, her heart gave a horrid little leap – in a strange kind of way she felt she owed it to Lucy to keep on nursing as a kind of perpetual piece of loyalty to her memory.

"I sound so bloody noble, don't I?" she said gloomily to Cal on the last weekend in August as they sat on the hot sands watching the tide go out. "I'm not, though. I'm scared of death, and yet I'm in the very profession where I'm likely to see it all the time. I hate the smell of blood and vomit, and if somebody starts to retch, I have to force myself not to do the same. Why did I ever think I could be a nurse?"

"Because you're good at it, that's why," Cal told her. "Because you have more compassion in your little finger than most people twice your age do. Don't belittle yourself, Daisy. We're going to need plenty like you pretty soon."

"You think I should volunteer to join a military nursing unit, then?" she said, following his thoughts. She shivered. "I don't think so! And besides, I'm probably not old enough."

Thank God, she thought.

"You may well be old enough before it ends," Cal told her. "Wars aren't fought and won in a day. The last one took four years, didn't it? You'll be twenty-one by then."

"Shut up, Cal. You're scaring me now. I don't want to think of a war lasting four years. Even Baz would be old enough to fight then. He'd be nineteen."

"Same as I am now."

They looked at one another. As if to remind them of Cal's passion for aviation, the steady drone of an aeroplane overhead made them both look up into the blue sky above the Bristol Channel, shielding their eyes against the bright sunlight.

"What's it like up there, feeling there's nothing between you and the ground but a piece of metal?" Daisy said suddenly.

310

"Marvellous," he said. "Providing the engine holds out and the wings don't fall off, of course. And as long as the pilot's had his eyes tested recently."

"Now you're making fun of me," Daisy said, grinning back, but feeling thankful that he was. You couldn't be gloomy all the time, especially when you were young and fancied yourself in love.

People were still bringing their children to the beach to make sandcastles with their buckets and spades and paying for rides on the Weston donkeys. Their screams of laughter were the same as always, and such idyllic scenes made thoughts of war still seem a million miles away.

"Come on, I'll race you to the ice-cream kiosk. Last one there buys them," Cal said, dragging her to her feet.

She tore off behind him, laughing wildly as their feet kicked up the soft sand that impeded their progress. So glad that she had met him, and knowing that whatever happened, she was going to marry him one day. She had quite made up her mind to that.

–

Elsie and Joe had already planned their wedding day. It had been nothing more than a vague, romantic idea at first, not at all logical, and one to be dismissed at once. What would the family think? What would her father say? And the new hat that Aunt Rose intended to have made wouldn't be needed for the occasion. Daisy and Immy wouldn't be bridesmaids, and then there was Joe's family…

Elsie had put up all sorts of arguments as to why they shouldn't do this. Joe's nice, homely parents would be so upset, and his Uncle Owen would probably have a blue fit and disown him. Not that they would have spared the time to make the long journey, Joe had said – especially Robert, who seemed to have an aversion to coming south anymore. It was too far, and his mother never travelled well. His father never travelled at all if he could help it.

"So what do you say, my love? Do we go ahead?" he asked. "You do realise that you'll be gaining a husband for a very short time."

"I know that," she murmured, knowing full well of his plans to enlist, and that he wouldn't put it off much longer. He had already informed his uncle of the fact, and Owen Preston had written to her father, telling him that in the event of his nephew going to war, Quentin was immediately to be made manager of the shop. It was the only thing that eased Elsie's mind about the whole thought of Joe being a soldier. His absence would mean a step up for Quentin, and put him back where he belonged, in charge of the shop.

She looked at Joe with clear brown eyes now.

"I'd rather have you as my husband for just a few days than not have you at all, Joe," she said softly. "And you'll always have me to come back to."

He caught her hand in his and touched her palm with his lips, enclosing the kiss inside it.

"That thought will be my talisman, my dearest. So we will make our plans."

–

The country awoke to the devastating news on Friday September first that the Nazi army had marched across the Polish border at dawn. Hitler's pact of non-aggression with Poland had been ignored, and in desperation Poland appealed to Britain and France for help. Both countries sent Germany ultimatums to withdraw that would expire in two days' time.

Entire communities began sending their children to the safety of the countryside in a panic. Evacuation had previously been an orderly affair, but what had been a comparative trickle before now became a flood, with roads and railways in danger of becoming clogged with the huge numbers of children and their teachers and helpers moving out of the cities with their assorted baggage, gas masks and labels. If many of the children thought of it as a great adventure, many more did not, and there was drama, tears and pandemonium at railway stations.

"We'll probably take another one," Rose declared on the phone to her brother. "We've plenty of room, and I've already put my name down at the Town Hall. The more the merrier, and the boys will enjoy having another friend to stay."

"You're mad," Quentin told her bluntly.

"Nonsense. I like having children around me. Besides—" She hesitated, not sure whether or not Daisy was in earshot. She decided that she wasn't. "You know that little Luckwell girl… It doesn't look too good for her, and her parents are going to be devastated if the worst happens."

"So you're surrounding yourself with children to soften the blow in case one of yours takes a bullet, are you?"

"Well, I wouldn't have put it quite so crudely! I prefer to say that this is my one chance of having the kind of family you and Frances had. Is that so wrong?"

After a moment, his voice was gruff.

"Not wrong at all, Rosie. Just take care of yourself, that's all. We can't afford to lose you."

"You don't get rid of a tough old bird like me that easily," she said briskly. "Now then, what's happened to Elsie lately? I thought she was going to make me a hat. Life goes on, Quentin, despite the worst that Hitler can do, and I still want to look my best for her wedding."

"She said something about coming to see you on the train on Saturday," he said with a frown. "I don't know if the news will alter her plans, though."

"She mustn't let it. But why don't we all come and see you on Sunday? If she arrives here, we'll bring her back with us – and we'll also bring one of my large apple pies, since it will be a bit of an invasion. Ronnie and Norman have never seen Bristol – and families should be together at important times."

It was her one concession to the fact that Adolf Hitler was already dictating their lives.

Elsie was being decidedly secretive lately, Quentin thought with a frown as he rang off. He had said as much to the Marys over afternoon tea a couple of days ago.

"Now that your daughters are young women, you can't expect them to confide in you as they did when they were children, Quentin," Mary Yard said gently. "Especially Elsie, since she's engaged to be married. You must remember what it was like in your youth."

He smiled ruefully, his eyes full of memories.

"Oh yes. Frances and I shared plenty of secrets that were ours alone. Not improper ones, you understand, but private things that would seem like nonsense to anyone else."

"That's it exactly," Mary Baxter agreed. "And when it comes to children, you have to let them go, don't you?"

For two widowed ladies who had never had children of their own, they were extremely canny, he thought approvingly. It was why he enjoyed their company so much. The young ones were his pride and joy, but there were times when a man needed mature company.

And that was all it was. He admitted that there had been a few idle moments when he had wondered what it might be like to marry again, and he sensed that Mary Yard had considered it as well. She was the one with whom he felt most compatible.

But he wasn't ready for marriage. And in a strange way, he knew exactly when she too had mentally withdrawn from the idea. A kind of mutual agreement had emerged between them, never spoken about, but undoubtedly there. It was a relief, a comfort, and it meant they could continue to enjoy these friendly little tête-à-têtes without any embarrassment.

"Elsie's going down to Weston on Saturday, and I dare say she'll stay at Rose's and come back with them on Sunday morning," he commented.

"Good for her. Who knows how many more such outings we'll be able to take?" Mary Yard said. "Have you started getting the shelter ready for occupancy, by the way?"

Quentin grimaced. "The shop is a useful supply source for that. I've got candles and matches and flashlights – not that we'll be able to use them out of doors, of course. And some tinned food and a tin opener, and water bottles – oh, and blankets in case we're there for any length of time."

"Goodness me, you make it sound like a siege," Mary Baxter exclaimed. "We're not expecting to stay in there forever, are we? It will be a little cramped, to say the least, and a bit earthy too. And tinned food, indeed! A camping stove and a kettle and tea would be more to the point, and some biscuits. It could be quite a little adventure really."

The three of them laughed, but the laughter didn't reach their eyes. All of them knew of old that it was going to be nothing like an adventure at all.

Chapter Nineteen

By Saturday the tension everywhere was almost tangible. The streets were strangely empty in many parts of the city. No one moved very far from their wireless sets, desperate to know if Neville Chamberlain's ultimatum to Hitler was going to be acknowledged and accepted.

Joe had decided that Preston's staff would prefer to be at home with their families, and since business was so slack the shop closed at lunchtime. He had had business of his own to attend to that morning and had left the closure to Quentin.

Elsie's small suitcase was already at Joe's digs, and she hugged Immy tightly when her sister drove her to the railway station.

"Be happy, Elsie," Immy said.

"Goodness me, it's just Aunt Rose's, and I'll only be away for one night," Elsie said, her eyes bright. But everyone knew that one night could change a person forever...

As soon as Immy had gone, Elsie waited impatiently for Joe to arrive. Bath was an elegant and beautiful city, he had told her, and Bath was where he had obtained the special licence that was going to make them man and wife later that afternoon.

Although Elsie had been tempted to confide in Immy, she would have bitten out her tongue first. But it was the most important secret she had ever kept from her sister.

Immy drove away, wondering if her deepest suspicions were true, and wishing her sister all the luck in the world if they were. She hadn't dared to ask. What she didn't know, she couldn't lie about.

She herself was frustrated that James Church still hadn't written to her. She knew it had only been a week, and that the needs of the army must come first, especially for someone training to be an officer, but it didn't help her feeling that perhaps it had all been a dream after all. Had James really implied that he loved her and wanted her? Or was she being a romantic fool?

Whatever it was, she felt an insurmountable need to be near his family and his home. She went straight to Helen's house, hoping they might have had news.

"No, old thing, he's gone incommunicado," Helen said. "Father says that's the army for you. We're not even at war yet, and already they're calling the tune… Sorry, darling," she added, seeing Immy's crestfallen face. "I didn't realise you were quite so smitten."

Immy tried to shrug it off with a laugh. *Smitten?* Was that the word for it? It seemed she had spent every waking moment since the fund-raising ball picturing James's face close to hers, breathing the same air, tasting his mouth, feeling the warmth of his arms around her.

Smitten? What a miserably ineffectual word that was for the strength of feeling she felt for James now! Stronger than anything she had ever felt for Morgan Raine. Deeper than she had ever imagined love could be. And yet she was also torn by the worry that she could be imagining the whole thing. Creating love out of need…

"Are you all right, Immy?" Helen's voice penetrated her thoughts. "Listen, I've had an idea. Well, it was Mother's, really. You know how good she is at these things."

"What things?"

"Organising and all that. The WVS is going to set up a sort of canteen at the railway station to provide drinks and cigarettes for soldiers coming home on leave or being sent home wounded. That sort of thing. They did it in the last war, apparently. Are you game to help, now that you're unemployed?"

Immy grimaced. "Thank you for reminding me! Your mother's obviously seeing war as a certainty. But if it is, I shall want to do something more useful than standing on a railway station dispensing tea!"

Helen looked at her steadily, her voice a shade cooler.

"Well, thank you for reminding *me* how useless I am! I'm sure I don't have your skills, but a bit of tea and sympathy goes a long way when you're facing the perils of war."

"Oh Helen, I'm sorry. I didn't mean to imply any such thing. Please don't let's quarrel. I'm so out of sorts today. Elsie's gone off somewhere, and although she hasn't confided in me I have a shrewd idea of what's happening."

"*Do* you?" Helen's scratchy mood changed at once. "Good Lord, Immy, you don't mean she and Joe have set up home together? Your father would never live down the scandal!"

"I don't mean that at all. Elsie would never do such a thing. But I do have my suspicions that they may be eloping."

"How utterly romantic!" Helen's eyes shone.

"How utterly irresponsible!" Immy snapped back. She immediately regretted it. "Oh Lord, I didn't mean that, either. I rather agree with you, but I'm frantic about how Father's going to take it if I'm right. Baz ran off without a word, and if Elsie's done the same—"

"He's still got you, darling."

"The sensible one, you mean." When Helen didn't answer immediately, her voice became more passionate. "I don't want to be boring, Helen! Don't you think I'd like to kick up my heels too, and run away and get married and live happily ever after? But sometimes I wonder if it will ever happen for me."

"Goodness you do need cheering up. Let's go for a walk on the Downs. Unless you'd prefer somewhere else," she added, remembering Immy's mother.

"Not at all. A good dose of fresh air is what I need."

But a shiver of premonition crept into her mind at that moment. Who knew how much longer any of them would be able to enjoy England's green and pleasant land, once Hitler set his greedy sights on them?

—

There were only five people inside the small country church just outside Bath that afternoon. The elderly vicar who was officiating, the bespectacled verger and his wife who were acting as witnesses, and the bride and groom.

Joe wore the brand-new army uniform he had collected that morning, and Elsie was ethereal in one of her mother's more demure stage dresses in soft white silk that hugged her body in fluid folds. Her sheaf of white lilies symbolised her purity.

In Joe's eyes, she had never looked more beautiful. And for Elsie, the sweet simplicity of the service and the empty little church seemed to emphasise even more the intimate relationship they were entering into.

She felt no more than a brief regret that there was no fanfare of rejoicing at their wedding. No family and friends to wish them well, or a feast to celebrate their nuptials. This was the true meaning of being joined by God, she thought, as the vicar intoned the solemn words. Committing their lives to one another…in sickness and in health…so long as they both should live.

She felt the coolness of the slim gold wedding band as Joe slid it on to her finger. He held it there while he said the words that bound them together for life.

"With this ring I thee wed. With my body I thee worship. And with all my worldly goods I thee endow."

His voice was thicker than usual as the vicar told him quietly that they were now man and wife, and that he might kiss his bride. He looked into Elsie's eyes for a long moment before taking her in his arms and holding her close.

In front of strangers it was the most chaste of kisses, a centuries-old ritual that each knew was a pledge of fidelity and love. It was a moment that would never come again, this first embrace as husband and wife.

Passion could wait, for they now had all the time in the world for belonging. No other thoughts of what might be happening in the wider world could dim the glory of this day.

–

Sunday morning in Rose's household was more hectic than usual. The small boys were taking an interminable time in getting ready to go to Bristol, squabbling over socks and sandals and generally making Rose wonder why she had ever thought having a family was such a desirable thing at all.

"If you three don't stop this, I'll box your ears for you," she bellowed finally, her nerves as frayed as everyone else's in the entire country. "Uncle Bertie's having enough trouble trying to persuade the car to behave, and heaven knows what's happened to Daisy."

"She's riding a horse at the farm and staying there all day," Teddy said, sulking. "She told you."

"Oh my, yes, so she did," Rose said, unusually flustered. "I'll forget my own head next. Now then, are we ready?"

"You said Elsie was coming to see me. Why didn't she come?" Teddy hollered next, determined to be difficult.

"Well, she must have had her reasons. We'll see her when we get you home. Come *along*, all of you."

She knew Bertie was uneasy about driving the old Morris motor with its growing habit of spluttering and stopping. It was always in doubt whether they would get to their destination or not.

"At this rate, we'll never get to Bristol before eleven o'clock," Rose snapped. "I so wanted us all to be together, and Quentin will be missing Baz as well as Daisy today."

"There's nothing we can do about it," Bertie told her. "If war's destined to happen, it will happen, whether or not we hear Chamberlain's words. Just hope this old blighter of a car gets us there before it finally gives up the ghost."

"Hope. Or pray," Rose muttered. "And since this is Sunday, that seems an appropriate comment to make."

She had never been a particularly religious woman, but right now, she was thinking that a few heartfelt prayers certainly wouldn't come amiss. And not just regarding the antics of their battered old car.

–

"It doesn't look as if your aunt and uncle are going to be here in time," Quentin said, as the hands of the clock moved inexorably round the dial towards eleven o'clock.

Immy looked at him nervously. What was he going to say when Elsie didn't arrive with them? It was more than a guess now, since she had looked in Elsie's room and discovered that her small suitcase had gone, together with her best clothes. She must have spirited them out of the house, and Immy was quite sure they weren't destined for Weston.

The final certainty had come when she discovered that Frances's filmy white dress that Elsie had coveted was also missing. Perfect for a wedding dress, her sister had said dreamily at the time. Lucky, lucky Elsie…

To Immy right now, the house seemed unbearably empty. Less than a year ago, it had been so full of life. Her darling mother had still been alive. Daisy and Teddy hadn't yet gone to live with Aunt Rose. Baz hadn't left home, and Elsie and herself were the stalwarts, boosting up her father as his beloved business was being taken over.

Now, in the sitting-room that seemed far too big, there were only the two of them. Her father was tinkering with the wireless set, cursing beneath his breath as he tried to maintain a clear reception. It was as if the whole country was holding its collective breath. And Immy suddenly couldn't bear it.

"Shall I ask the Marys to come and join us, Father?" she said. "I'm sure they would appreciate the company."

"If you wish, my dear," he said abstractedly.

She fled upstairs and knocked on the Marys' door. It suddenly seemed important to be surrounded by people on today of all days – unless you were Elsie and Joe, of course. She gave a fleeting thought to how they might be spending this Sunday morning, and just as quickly blotted out the vicarious images. It was private.

It seemed that the Marys were just as thankful to join them downstairs, and at eleven o'clock they all sat silently around the wireless set as the premier's crackling words were emitted. Words that were to change their lives forever.

The voice was as pedantic as ever, and as it went on, Immy found herself hating the deliberate, emotionless sound of it.

"This morning, the British Ambassador in Berlin handed the German government a final note stating that unless we heard from them by eleven o'clock that they were prepared at once to withdraw their troops from Poland a state of war would exist between us.

"I have to tell you now that no such undertaking has been received, and that consequently this country is at war with Germany. You can imagine what a bitter blow it is to me that all my long struggle to win peace has failed."

There was so much more. There were explanations and commitments and the outline of future plans, but Immy took in very little of it. Tomorrow, the speech would be in all the newspapers, and they could all devour it in its entirety.

For now, she was aware of the soft sound of Mary Baxter's tearful sniffling and noticed the way her father had squeezed Mary Yard's hand for a moment, as memories of past conflicts were revived. These three had already been through another war, while she had not.

In a ridiculous way, it excluded her. She was momentarily the outsider, and it filled her heart with a huge emptiness. Then her father noticed her ashen face and hugged her close.

"It's a bitter blow, but hardly unexpected, my love. We'll get through it together, the same as we've always done," he said in a rough voice.

As she nodded wordlessly, he went on more firmly.

"We've always pulled together, and we won't fail our country now. Whatever has to be done, will be done."

"Amen to that," Mary Yard murmured.

They stayed talking quietly for nearly an hour, listening to comments on the wireless from those who possessed more insight into what was about to happen. They tried to believe and accept that Mr Chamberlain had done the only thing possible in the circumstances. Finally, as a commotion began to be heard outside, Mary Yard glanced at her friend.

"I think your family has arrived at last, Quentin, so we'll leave you. Actually, we've been discussing whether or not to stay in the city, so now we must make up our minds."

Immy looked at her father sharply to see if this news might disturb him, but he merely nodded and let them go.

She turned thankfully as the three boisterous small boys burst into the room, with a red-faced Rose and Bertie close behind.

"What a morning!" Rose exclaimed. "I swear I thought we'd never get here. The car's almost expiring! But we know the bad news, my dears. The placards are already out, and there are people on the streets, some of them weeping openly."

She said this last quietly, not wanting to alarm the boys.

"I'm sorry Daisy's not with us," she went on, "but she wanted to be at the Luckwell farm with Lucy's parents."

"Where's Elsie?" Bertie said, finally getting a word in, and catching his breath after his battles with the temperamental car and three equally temperamental children.

"She's with you, isn't she?" Quentin said.

Rose stared. "No. When she didn't arrive yesterday we simply assumed she'd changed her mind about coming to Weston. It was all rather vague, anyway. Isn't she here?"

"She is not," Quentin said grimly. "I haven't seen her since yesterday, when Imogen took her to the railway station."

They all looked at Immy now, as accusingly as if she had committed a sin – when in reality she had done nothing at all, she thought indignantly.

She couldn't help thinking how ironic it was that domestic family problems could so quickly overshadow that of a nation's catastrophe. But perhaps it was better so, before imagination took them to places no one wanted to see.

"I don't know where Elsie is!" she said defensively. "I merely did as she asked and took her to the railway station."

"But if she wasn't going to Weston, then where was she going?" Quentin demanded. "You must have some idea, girl."

"I don't. I didn't."

Her mouth trembled, realising she was being treated like an accomplice now. It was all so unfair.

Her stomach felt as if it had turned to water, and all the romance of a suspected elopement was turning into something sordid.

"If the girl's really missing, shouldn't we inform the police, Quentin?" Bertie was saying. "There are some strange characters about these days."

"No," Immy said sharply. "I'm sure that's not necessary. Elsie would feel foolish if she was tracked down like a common criminal."

"She'll be a victim rather than a criminal if something's happened to her!" Rose snapped. "Was she alone or was she with someone? You must know her friends, Imogen. Think, girl."

Angry at the implied accusation that she was partly to blame, Immy took a deep breath. Now was the time; there was no more avoiding it. She spoke directly to Quentin.

"Father, this is only a guess, but I suspect that Elsie and Joe may have decided to get married without any fuss. Some of her best clothes are missing."

Rose exclaimed loudly. "The thoughtless hussy! How could she do this in such terrible times?"

"It could have something to do with wanting to feel she belonged to Joe before he went to war," Immy retorted, her eyes sparkling with fury now. "Maybe you've forgotten how it feels to be young and in love, Aunt Rose."

"Imogen, you will apologise to your aunt at once," Quentin roared. He had been silent with shock until this moment.

"No, the girl's right, Quentin," Rose said quickly. "But to go off without telling anyone *is* deceitful."

"And romantic and reckless," Immy went on relentlessly. "They were already engaged, and if they chose to bring the date forward to thwart Mr Hitler's plans, it's their lives, isn't it? *Daddy?*"

She pleaded with him not to hate Elsie for what she had done. They had always been such a close family unit, and even when they were apart, they were still strong. She willed him to remember that. She would defend Elsie to the death, just as she had supported Baz, and assured her father it would be good for Daisy and Teddy to go to Aunt Rose's.

She saw his mouth give the smallest twist.

"You were always a persuasive young baggage, Imogen. Well, what's done is done, even though I think the manner of it is unforgivable. I shall have strong words to say to Joe about it when they deign to contact us."

Since no one else could think of anything else to say on the matter, they reverted in some relief to more urgent thoughts of the future now that they were officially at war.

"I shall offer my services, of course," Immy said at once. "Now that Mr Harris has gone to Cornwall in partnership with his brother, I shall need to find some different work."

"There'll be no shortage of that," Rose said. "Women always come into their own when the menfolk have gone away to fight. I shall start a knitting circle for soldiers' comforts, and munition factories will want plenty of volunteers."

It wasn't really what Immy had in mind, but she didn't think now was the time to suggest that she and Helen might apply to be official drivers in one of the women's services. It was an idea that had been catching hold of her lately, and just as Elsie felt she would be mentally if not physically closer to Joe once they were married, Immy felt she would be a touch closer to James if she was in the same line of business. More or less.

She bit her lip, thinking how quickly life could change. Yesterday they hadn't been at war, and now they were. Yesterday she had been thinking vaguely that she might have to work in Preston's temporarily, and now she was thinking of leaving home herself and spreading her wings in a way she had never considered before. It was unnerving to think that war could be the catalyst for such changes.

The telephone rang. Quentin answered it, and eventually returned to the sitting-room with a flushed face.

"That was your sister," he said abruptly to Immy. "You were right. She and Joe were married by special licence yesterday and are staying in a hotel in Bath until Tuesday, when he has to report to his regiment. Joe enlisted several days ago, so the honeymoon will be very short-lived."

Immy had to ask. "Daddy, you did give them your blessing, didn't you?"

"How could I not? Despite her distress at having to confess to me, I couldn't miss the happiness in her voice. And she'll be back home with us on Tuesday evening."

But not in the same way as before, Immy thought. Not now that she's known Joe's love and become a part of him in the most intimate way a man and a woman can share themselves. She envied them that closeness so much.

The telephone didn't seem to stop ringing all day. Baz was as brash as ever, telling them that he had heard the news, and that he wished he was old enough to join up. Right now he was about to leave for the Cornish fishing grounds, but he promised to come and visit them as soon as his boat returned to Bristol.

Joe's distraught parents got through from Yorkshire after an interminable wait, to tell them Joe had managed to call them, and they hoped the Caldwells weren't too upset. Oh, and there was the war, they added, almost as an afterthought…

Daisy rang from the Luckwells to check that everyone was all right, and to say that Mrs Luckwell was taking the news badly, since she'd lost a brother in the last lot.

"That's how she put it," Daisy said to Immy. "Odd, isn't it? I think she's glad I'm here, though, so I'm staying for the rest of the day. And the best news is that Lucy's much better."

"I'm glad. You're a good pal, Daisy," Immy said softly.

"Oh, I know. A proper little saint, aren't I?" she answered breezily, covering her embarrassment. "Anyway, tell Aunt Rose that if I'm not back when they get home, she knows where I'll be. Love to you all, by the way."

"Oh, and Daisy—"

But she'd gone before Immy could tell her about Elsie and Joe. It didn't matter. Aunt Rose would do it far more eloquently face to face. She hung up the phone slowly.

Without warning, she was completely out of sorts again. In a kind of limbo. As deflated as if all the air had just been let out of her lungs.

She told herself severely it was hardly surprising. Her country had just gone to war, and nothing was ever going to be the same again.

But it was more than that. It was the feeling that everyone had something to do or say, someone to hold or to touch, when she had nothing and no one. The family was all around her, and yet she had never felt so alone.

She realised that the house was very quiet now, and there was only the occasional creak of floorboards from the Marys' rooms above. She hadn't even been aware of the moment when the grown-ups had gone into the garden to join the boys, though when she concentrated she could hear the sounds of the children's chatter, muted, as if they came from a long distance away. She could hear the deeper murmur of the adults' voices, more serious but determined not to let the trauma of this day affect three small lives.

In her head she could hear the echo of her mother, who had once filled this house with joy and laughter, and she blinked back the brief, stinging tears.

She felt as though the place was suddenly stifling her and knew that if she stayed inside for much longer, she would go quietly mad. She had to get out.

"I'm going to see Helen," she called out to her father. "I won't be gone long, and I'll see you all before you leave, Aunt Rose."

"It's hardly polite to leave when we have guests, Imogen," Quentin began, but Rose put her hand on his arm, stilling his words.

"Let her go, Quentin. She needs to find her own peace."

"That's a bloody peculiar remark for anyone to make, if I may say so," he objected roughly, the words disguising his affection for her. "Considering we've just entered a war."

"I know," she said, her smile wavering and her eyes suddenly blurring with tears. "But then, I was always a peculiar woman, wasn't I, brother dear?"

—

Imogen kept her head down as she pedalled into the sudden blustery wind on her way to Helen's home.

She could have walked, but she didn't want to encounter people she knew, who would want to discuss this morning's announcement. She could have borrowed her father's car, but right now she wouldn't trust herself to drive sensibly. She rode hard, and she was out of breath long before she approached the lovely old house where the Church family lived.

There was a sudden noise from someone's garden, and a cluster of birds in a nearby tree flapped their wings and rose in a grey cloud into the sky. She wasn't a visionary, but in those few horrific seconds she had a weird sense of what the future might hold.

War clouds overhead, and the clear blue yonder being filled with the droning engines of enemy planes. Bombs being dropped. Buildings being torn apart as if they were as insubstantial as cardboard, reducing them to nothing but rubble and choking dust…and their occupants with them…destroying Bristol…bringing carnage and death to a once beautiful city…

She slewed her bicycle to a stop, shaking all over. If she hadn't, she knew she would have run into something. She was shocked by her own feelings of impotence and rage at that moment. Everyone had expected war for so long that some had almost become complacent. As if it was never really going to happen. It was all men's talk. All bravado.

Had she actually been one of them all this time? Never taking it as seriously as she should? Never thinking it would really affect her, or her family, even pooh-poohing Helen's talk of dispensing tea for soldiers on railway stations as something of a silly pastime for wealthy girls? How *could* she have been so blind? So shamefully self-centred…

"Imogen, by all that's wonderful! I was on my way to see you. Darling, you look so white. Are you ill?"

She felt someone take her bicycle away from her to prop it against a tree, not realising that she had been gripping the handlebars so tightly that she almost fell without their support.

But not quite. Because by then, that someone's arms were around her, and she was being pressed to his chest. The gruesome visions that had held her captive for those awful moments cleared, and she clutched James Church tightly as she gasped out his name.

"Oh James, I can't believe it's you. What are you doing here? I thought you were far away. You haven't written, and you promised—"

She was babbling incoherently, like a lovesick idiot, and she couldn't seem to stop.

"I know, and I'm sorry," he said, his voice vibrating against her cheek. "Field manoeuvres don't leave much time or opportunity for writing letters, I'm afraid."

"Not even one?" she said, brittle with unreasoning anger now, despite herself.

"Not even one. And I've only got a mouldy twelve-hour pass now before we get our orders for embarkation. But it doesn't mean I'm not thinking of you, Immy, darling. I think of you all the time. And you mustn't worry if you don't hear from me as often as you'd like."

She moved back from him a little, but he still held her close. She looked up into his handsome face and couldn't miss the determination there. He was like all the rest. He was St George and Sir Galahad all rolled into one. Eager to go, eager to fight, despite the fact he might be killed. And that was something she couldn't bear to think about.

"I don't want you to die, James," she said, hearing the tremor in her voice and despising herself for it.

"Well, I don't plan to, not if I have you to come home to," he said laughingly. The laughter faded a little, and he looked down at her less assuredly. "Do I, Immy?"

"You know you do," she whispered.

He bent his head to hers, and she felt the sweetest kiss on her lips, uncaring that they were in public, for there was no one around to see.

"Do you want to go and tell the folks?" he said softly.

She shook her head. "I don't want to tell anyone just yet. Let it be our secret, just for an hour or so. Except—" she went on, but hesitated, wondering if he would think her completely crazy if she said what was in her heart. Even as she felt her cheeks go hot, however, she knew she had to say it, and it was important that he understood.

"Could we take a walk over the Downs? I want to cherish the sense of freedom we still have."

"And you want to tell your mother's spirit that you've found your true love at last," he said, as if he could read every unspoken word.

She looked at him in real astonishment, and with a deep respect for such perception. "How did you know?"

"Call it intuition. Call it anything you like, but when two hearts are in tune, something far deeper than mere words flows between them."

She was more moved than she could say, never expecting a man to use such emotive words. But then, she had never known a man like James before. She had known him all her life, yet it was clearly going to take forever to learn about him. It was a thought to fill her with joy, the first positive thought in her head on this momentous day.

"I do love you, James," she said daringly, forgetting all about the protocol of waiting for a man to say it first. It seemed such a silly convention now.

"And I love you. I always have, and I always will. Even when we're far apart, and whatever the future holds, you must always remember that and take heart, my love. Promise me."

"I will," Imogen said. "Always."